GUIDED WEAPONS

By the same author
ROCKET PROPULSION
FRONTIER TO SPACE

A USAF tactical missile, the Martin MATADOR is boosted from a zero-length launcher by a solid-propellant rocket and then flies for 500 miles under the sustaining thrust of an Allison turbo-jet engine.

(Photo. Glenn L. Martin Co.)

Frontispiece

GUIDED

WEAPONS

ERIC BURGESS, F.R.A.S.

NEW YORK

THE MACMILLAN COMPANY

To
MICHAEL

PREFACE

THE survival of our present human civilization depends upon the prevention of a further global conflict. Whether or not the concept of the deterrent power of technological weapons of mass destruction is sound only history will decide. Yet it is undoubtedly fashionable to regard science as synonymous with salvation.

That long-range guided weapons can be a part of a nation's armoury has now been demonstrated. In September 1956, for example, the third stage of a multi-stage rocket having a REDSTONE as a launching stage achieved a range of 3,000 miles (4,800 km.) and a peak altitude of 400 miles (640 km.).

With the limitation that it must be accepted that a modern guided weapon could never be designed from unclassified material, an attempt has been made to introduce the reader to the fundamentals, both historical and technical, on which guided weapons are based. An aim of the book has been to show how guided weapons have been developed from ideas arising at the end of World War II when a demand arose for machines which would be able to accomplish things for which man himself, physically or mentally, was unsuited.

While many sources of information are gratefully acknowledged the views presented must be regarded as the author's own and not necessarily agreeing with official or industrial ideas on the subject.

If this book encourages more students and newly qualified men to start thinking actively about guided weapons and their problems, if it enables the intelligent layman to appreciate why his taxes have not yet secured his cities beneath missile screens, it will have achieved the author's purpose.

E. BURGESS

Los Angeles,
October, 1956

7

ACKNOWLEDGEMENTS

THE production of this book would have been impossible without the aid of the information supplied by the Public Relation and Press Officers of many companies in Britain and the United States including:

Armstrong Siddeley Motors Ltd., American Brass Company, Bristol Aeroplane Co. Ltd., Brooks & Perkins Inc., Boeing Airplane Company, Bell Telephone Laboratories, Allied Chemical & Dye Corporation, Bell Aircraft Corporation, Bakelite Ltd., Curtiss-Wright Corporation, Cook Electric Company, Convair Division of General Dynamics Corporation, Chance Vought Aircraft Inc., Ethyl Corporation, Elliott Bros. (London) Ltd., Fairey Aviation Ltd., Fairchild Guided Missile Division, Fibreglass Ltd., Grand Central Rocket Co., Gyromechanisms Inc., Graseby Instruments Ltd., Hydro-Aire Inc., Hamilton Standards Division United Aircraft Corporation, International General Electric Company, Imperial Chemical Industries Ltd., International Rectifier Corporation, Kollsman Instrument Corporation, Arthur D. Little Inc., Glenn L. Martin Co., Magnesium Elektron Ltd., Marquardt Aircraft Co., North American Aviation Inc., D. Napier & Son Ltd., Oerlikon Machine Tool Works Buehrle & Co., Potter Aeronautical Company, Ryan Aeronautical Company, J. W. Roberts Ltd., Remington Rand Ltd., Reaction Motors Inc., Sir W. G. Armstrong Whitworth Ltd., Saunders Roe Ltd., Sperry Gyroscope Co. Ltd., Solartron Electronic Group Ltd., Thiokol Chemical Corporation, Telegraph Condenser Co. Ltd., Transistor Products Inc., and Venner Accumulators Ltd.

Thanks are also due to the following gentlemen and agencies who have made information, photographs and material available for publication in this book or have granted permission for it to be used.

Dr. C. G. Bull of the Canadian Armament Research and Development Establishment, Mr. A. L. Thomas of the Applied Physics Laboratory, Johns Hopkins University, Mr. W. T. Bonney of the National Advisory Committee for Aeronautics, Mr. H. R. F. Brett of the British Embassy, Washington, Mr. R. Jacoby of the United States Information Service, Mr. C. M. Huntly of the Information Branch, British Ministry of Supply, Mr. H. Beale of the Australian Supply Ministry, Dr. M. P. Allen of the National Physical Laboratory, the Editor of *The Times Science Review*, The Editor of *The Engineer*, the Editor of *Aircraft*, Colonel Puget, the French Air Attaché in London, the Secretary and Council of the Institution of Mechanical Engineers, the Naval Research Laboratory and the Information Branches of the United States Navy, Army and Air Force.

Also to my Wife for assistance at all stages, and,

The Staff of the publishers who really make the book possible.

E.B.

CONTENTS

11

CHAPTER I

SYSTEMS AND MISSILES

◎

FEAR of the consequences of a future air war dominates the military thought of all nations. National survival in the event of attack can only be assured if 100 per cent interception can be obtained. Conventional fighter aircraft and anti-aircraft weapons are inadequate for such a task, and a new answer to the problem had to be found. This answer appears to be the guided weapon system.

But guided weapons act in two ways. Properly developed they should not only assure an adequate defence but also act as a deterrent against aggression because they can give instant retaliation.

At a cost of countless man-hours in both East and West, guided weapons are bringing extended peace through a technical stalemate whereby either side is in a position to start off a cycle of strategic missiles which in a few hours could inflict irrecoverable damage to aggressor and defender alike.

Guided weapon systems are not mystical. They are the logical outcome of technical progress in many fields which has made their development possible at the time when that same technological progress was making their development necessary.

During World War II the Germans first used rocket-propelled and radio-controlled glider bombs against Allied shipping. A guided missile became operational. It was the Hs. 293 rocket-propelled air-to-sea bomb. Essentially this missile consisted of a conventional bomb built into a small aircraft fuselage which was equipped with wings, control surfaces, and an underslung rocket motor. The aim of the designers was to produce a large bomb which could be launched from aircraft and directed against shipping, while at the same time the parent aircraft could remain out of range of the guns of the vessel which was being attacked. Radio commands to the missile formed a control system in order to overcome the difficulties presented by evasive action which the ships might take after the bomb had been launched. Large German aircraft such as the 'He. 111', 'He. 117', 'Do. 217', and 'FW. 200' were equipped to carry one of these missiles under each wing.[1]

A whole family of guided missiles was being developed by the end of World War II but most had not reached the stage of production. Some missiles were controlled by wire, others had internal gyroscopic controls and even television eyes, while propulsion units included various types of solid and liquid propellant rockets, and a pulse-jet. Free falling radio- and wire-controlled bombs were also under development.

Moreover, missiles were being made for defence as well as attack; several air-to-air and surface-to-air vehicles were in advanced stages of development.

For example the Hs. 298 air-to-air rocket was designed early in 1944 and although mass production was planned for 1945 development and testing had not been completed by the end of the war. Originally this missile was intended for use with a liquid-propellant rocket unit which was later modified to use a solid-propellant motor and to be launched from fighter aircraft against the attacking bomber formations which were crippling the German war effort. The design called for it to be released at a range of about one mile (1·6 km) from the target and to be controlled by radio signals from the parent aircraft. It was essentially a miniature aircraft, very different from the modern concept of a guided missile. Construction was of sheet metal while a step was included in the fuselage design so that the exhaust from the rocket unit would clear the conventional tail surfaces.

A design more in keeping with modern trends was the X-4 air-to-air missile, one of a series named from X-1 to X-7, the other members of which were all air-to-surface weapons. An almost tubular cast aluminium centre section housed the propellant tanks and pressure tanks. Riveted to it were aluminium supports to which the four laminated wooden wings were bolted. These had a pronounced sweep back; two carried flares at the tips, while the other pair carried bobbins from which a control cable was paid out during flight. The nose consisted of a warhead and an acoustic proximity fuse, while the rear fairing enclosed the propellant feed lines and the rocket motor at the tail. In this section were control gyroscopes, storage batteries, and the servomechanisms for the control of spoilers which interrupted the flow of air over a cruciform tail. Propulsive power was obtained from a BMW 109–548 bi-propellant rocket motor using 98 per cent nitric acid and a mixture of tri-ethylamine and oxide *m*-xylidine.

The first model of the X-4 was constructed in 1944, but although this weapon was ready for mass production at the end of the war, it was, in fact, never used operationally. In order to minimize difficulties of handling the corrosive nitric acid by service personnel an alternative version was planned in which a Schmidding diglycol solid-propellant rocket unit, 109–603, was to be used.

For defence, the other class of weapons comprises the ground-to-air missiles on which so much accent is placed to-day. German developments in this field ranged from the tiny unguided TAIFUN to the larger RHEINTOCHTER and the WASSERFALL. There was also a winged vehicle known as the SCHMETTERLING which was under development by Henschell. It had a liquid-propellant rocket and used solid propellant boosters to achieve a launching from a zero-length launcher. The operational ceiling was reported as about 35,000 ft (10,500 m) with an absolute ceiling of 50,000 ft (15,000 m). Maximum speed was obtained just after take-off when the booster units were operating, but this was subsonic. The horizontal range varied with the warhead, an average value being 20 miles (32 km) for a 50-lb (22·5 kg) warhead.

The largest anti-aircraft rocket was the RHEINTOCHTER of which two types were in development. R.1 had an all-up weight of 3,860 lb (1,750 kg), while R.3 was a smaller rocket of only 2,150 lb (976 kg). These were both large rockets built in two stages, a large booster followed by the missile proper. Both boosters and missiles were fitted with huge stabilizing fins, while control was effected by four small surfaces at the missile's nose.

Germany also had the WASSERFALL supersonic liquid-propellant surface-to-air missile, the ENZIAN a pilotless aircraft, and the NATTER. The last named was a small aircraft-type piloted vehicle.

The final class of guided weapons, the surface-to-surface vehicle was also represented in Germany by the well-known A-series of missiles,[2] the most advanced of which was the A-4, popularly called the V-2. This series consisted of liquid-propellant, long-range, rocket vehicles which followed ballistic trajectories, though A-9 was a more advanced project, the range of which it was intended to extend by the use of wing surfaces which would bring the missile into a protracted glide when it re-entered the appreciable atmosphere on the downward leg of its trajectory.

In addition there was the multi-stage solid-propellant RHEINBOTE,[3] a ramjet which was known as the TROMSDORF GESCHOSS, and, of course, the V-1 pulse-jet.

By the end of World War II, several companies in the United States of America were also working on guided weapon projects, especially with a view to the defence of carriers and warships against *Kamikaze* attacks. But guided weapons cannot be developed quickly and none of these weapons saw a great deal of use before the close of hostilities. The Allies were hampered by lack of suitably advanced missile propulsion plants because of their neglect of the rocket and the ramjet.

We see then, that the various classes of guided missiles had been established in Germany by the end of World War II and that some had even been tested in combat. With the realization that a secure peace had not been obtained, with the advent of nuclear weapons and other means of mass destruction, the large powers had to commence organizing guided weapon programmes. Some were very slow to get under way, Britain for example, probably because responsible people in authority still held the 'thin red line' mentality. Others like the United States of America and Soviet Russia, pressed on rapidly from the German work and, after quickly testing many types of vehicles, they soon were able to bring interim guided missile systems into production in order to act as a means of security until more advanced systems could be perfected.

Today the guided weapon industry absorbs a large proportion of the scientific and technical man-power of the industrialized nations. Modern missiles bear little relation to the early German versions. Nearly all are supersonic and use advanced propulsion systems and complex electronic devices for guidance purposes. The missile itself is now regarded as a part of a weapons system rather than an isolated vehicle.[4] Both its design and its performance are linked closely with other means of defence. When we speak of a guided weapon defence system we must include the early warning radar screens, radar interrogation, the outer ring of bases for interceptor fighters with their air-to-air missiles, the inner radar and its associated 'last-ditch' surface-to-air missiles. (*Fig.* 1.1.)

FIG. 1.1. *Modern anti-aircraft devices include liquid-propellant rocket vehicles which can execute rapid manœuvres and ride along radar beams to intercept high-flying transonic bombers.*

(Photo. Oerlikon Buhrle & Co.)

The men who have been planning guided missiles have had a task of immense difficulty before them. Not only were there tremendous technical problems to be overcome but the guided missile industry had to contend with the military mind. This latter can unintentionally be the greatest obstacle to progress because military men justifiably are loath to change weapons during peace-time.[5] They find it out of the question to regard proven weapons as obsolete and to give all-out support to new weapons which may appear superlative on paper or in controlled tests but are untried in battle. This attitude is understandable because bombers and guns have been tested in combat while a new weapon like a guided missile can be something completely unorthodox, and in the case of the missile, almost alien to warfare as it now takes away all ideas of human heroics and valour.

Yet somehow, despite a certain amount of antagonism, which more often shows itself as indifference, the guided missile industry has had to be prepared to design weapons which can be put into immediate production when finally the military leaders call for them, that is when the realization dawns that potential enemies—or enemies in time of war—have similar devices included in their armouries.

On the other hand, missiles do not represent the ultimate defence. To ignore guided missile potentiality is fatal to national defence, but it would be as equally as disastrous to concentrate all efforts in the construction of a Maginot Line of missile launching sites. Security from intercontinental ballistic missiles with nuclear warheads is pointless if a nation finds itself succumbing to bacteriological or chemical weapons planted within its territory by enemy agents or by traitors.

Missile development must be planned so long as the political leaders of the world are unable to ensure world friendship amongst nations. Scientists have accordingly to develop all possible technological weapons and defences which are needed to deter aggressors and to give maximum protection in the event of war.

With the development of guided missiles, especially of long-range weapons, an entirely different view had to be taken of global conflict between technological powers.[6] The first warning of danger may be only available to the defences minutes, or even seconds, before an all-out attack is unleashed.

In the case of the intercontinental ballistic missile it appears unlikely that any rapid development of a positive defence can be assumed. The only hope for survival is in the negative one of the threat of instant retaliation; the possibility of flinging similar missiles with their thermo-nuclear warheads to destroy the war-making potential of the enemy. This threat must act as a deterrent to would-be aggressors.

It appears logical at the present moment that any future conflict will start with a massive attack aimed at complete paralysis of the nations or section of the world against which it is directed, to destroy first the will to retaliate and then the means of retaliation. At the present time we cannot be sure if attack will come from conventional aircraft or by means of intercontinental missiles. Guided weapon defence then has to take two forms, the positive development of anti-aircraft and anti-missile systems which can intercept and destroy enemy raiders as far as possible from the target areas, and the negative one of producing deterrents in the form of nuclear-warheaded intercontinental weapons which can deliver a thermo-nuclear attack anywhere on the globe within thirty minutes or so of any aggression.

As far as positive defence is concerned the ideal to be aimed at is a kill for every missile dispatched. At the present time missiles are not so good as that.[7] Hence current practice must be to build up a formidable missile force which will outweigh the attack potential of any possible enemy. Enough missile launchers have to be available to intercept any likely number of attacking planes or air-to-ground missiles. Moreover there must be the earliest possible warning so that one or two attempts may be made at interception before the aggressors reach the target areas.

The case of the defence of the United Kingdom is very different from that of the North American Continent. The British Isles represent one of the most concentrated industrial areas in the world and they are, moreover, completely surrounded by sea. A modern technique is to launch missiles from submarines[8] and this could levy a tremendous toll on Britain in a very short time. In the defence of Britain, therefore, a great part has still to be played by the Royal Navy even in these times of air power. Submarines must be kept away from these Islands, sufficiently far away for the guided missile and fighter defences to be able at least to have one attempt at interception before submarine-launched missiles can approach the coastline.

Fig. 1.2. *Many modern missiles also use ramjet propulsion devices. This series of photographs shows a test vehicle launched by booster rockets. The diameter of the propulsion unit was 6 in and two units were mounted in tandem. A ballistic trajectory was followed by the vehicle which was launched from a twin-railed ramp by means of two 7·5 in cordite rockets. The top photograph shows the booster rockets accelerating the missile to supersonic speed; the second picture is at boost separation, while the final picture shows the vehicle flying solely on the ramjets.*

(Photos. Bristol Aeroplane Co.)

20

Britain must be well screened from the European side, yet it should not be lightly forgotten that a two-stage rocket such as the Bumper-WAC (fired in 1949) would be able to reach any part of Britain when fired from 500 miles (800 km) away in Europe. Moreover nowadays there are better long-range rockets than this.

From statements made at various times by responsible officials it appears that Britain's defence system is being developed in the following logical manner required by her unique position in Western Europe.

High priority is being given to the production of air-to-air missiles which can be carried by all-weather patrol fighters[9] and will certainly spell destruction to conventional bombers. (*Fig.* 1.2.)

Secondly, long-range ground-to-air interceptor missiles which can destroy supersonic aircraft and missiles travelling up to two or three times the speed of sound before they reach the coastline. (*Fig.* 1.3.)

FIG. 1.3. *Test vehicles have been used extensively for the development of guided weapon systems. This photograph shows an unnamed British rocket test vehicle being fired at the Long-Range Weapons Establishment at Woomera. Rockets like this can be used for ground-to-air interception.*
(Photo. L.R.W.E. Salisbury)

Finally, the last ditch defence, short-range but highly efficient ground-to-air missiles which can be placed at the ready on the periphery of defence areas to engage attackers which may penetrate the outer defences.

A number of other branches of guided weapon development include missiles for the protection of capital ships, anti-submarine missiles, and long-range work on the intercontinental missiles.[10] Also the high-speed bombers will be equipped with guided bombs or air-to-surface missiles.

In America, on the other hand, the vast distances which a potential enemy must cover before he can reach any important target area, gives the defence systems adequate time in which to take action, and also plenty of space in which to destroy the attackers where they will cause least damage to cities and industries.

Unlike aircraft development, tradition and precedent play only a minor role in the development of guided missiles.[11] Missile design involves, indeed, most of the physical sciences but it requires a search for new answers in even the long established branches of science.

So far the main innovation in missile technology has been the guidance systems, the missile 'brains'. These need associated sensory organs and means of control, and may have to think 10,000 times as fast as the human brain. Yet most of missile equipment is not new. There are electric motors, accumulators, switches, radio valves, propulsion units and aerodynamic controls. To begin with commercial equipment had to be used but was often found wanting. Essentially this was because missiles develop a great deal of noise and heat, they undergo severe vibrations and high accelerations. Under these conditions commercially available equipment often failed and had to have considerable modification. Now new equipment is being designed especially for use in missiles and thus it is improving reliability.

At first sight one might think that because a missile carries no pilot it need not be so reliable as a normal aircraft. This is indeed not so. If a fault occurs in a normal aircraft the pilot can often improvise and make allowances arising from his experience. His mastery of the art of flying can more often than not compensate for the failure of his machine and enable him to make it safely complete its mission.

There is no such inherent adaptability in the electronic brain of a missile. It can only do the job for which it has been designed. Moreover, the failure of a single component may cause the missile not to reach its objective and thus allow a fusion bomb to destroy hundreds of thousands of people. Hence all missile components must be absolutely reliable. But although they need reliability, they only need it for a comparatively short time, a factor which does ease the problem. For example, such things as radio valves can be overloaded, yet if specially selected they can give service during the flight in the missile because they are normally designed for a much longer life. A reduction in the demanded useful life by a factor of one hundred permits satisfactory operation under gross overloads.

Following this tendency it has been found possible to design missiles to the ultimate strengths of the materials employed rather than their yield strengths, simply because most missiles are short-period one-shot devices. This results, of course, in a considerable reduction of weight.

Another important factor in guided weapons is that all components of the missile system must not only be individually reliable but also compatible. For example one does not want the missile released by one interceptor to attack another of the defending aircraft. Neither is it desired that several defence missiles should all home on one raider while a companion passes through the defence with impunity.

Missile systems which operate satisfactorily on the laboratory bench may be completely inadequate in the field when operated by service personnel under operational conditions. It is comparatively simple to design a missile which can be fired by trained scientists, at their convenience, against a target drone which is sent over the launching area when all is ready for the test. But it is an entirely different story if the missile has to be readied and fired by not-so-highly trained service men who have to be roused on a stormy night to launch missiles against a completely unexpected mixture of decoys and nuclear-weapon-carrying aircraft. These will be taking every possible evasive action, dropping 'window' and using other radar interfering devices, and may even have chosen a period of magnetic disturbances for their attack.

Far from criticizing the guided missile people for slowness in producing a foolproof push-button defence, we should compliment them on the tremendous progress which has been made so far; especially in view of the undoubted difficulties both political and technical with which they have had to contend. Moreover there has been the stupefying pall of security which has prevented unrestricted discussion of their work,[12] while it is well known that scientific discussion is the greatest aid to progress. And secrecy has prevented new engineers and scientists from being attracted to missile work. The development of a perfect guided weapon system also needs almost unlimited funds. As will later be discussed in this book, the problems are immense and embrace many technical and scientific fields. (*Fig.* 1.4.) The recruitment of technical man-power was

(*a*) *Aerodynamic studies are made with missiles as with this NACA model which was flown to investigate boundary layer characteristics and heating at supersonic speeds.* (Photo. N.A.C.A.)

(*b*) *Also missile test vehicles enable controls and instrumentations to be tried out as with the GAPA series which led to the production of the BOMARC. Here is an early GAPA research vehicle being prepared for firing at Great Salt Desert, Utah.* (Photo. Boeing Airplane Co.)

FIG. 1.4

also not enough. The recruits had to be trained in the missile art. In missile work compatibility of components is essential, and men were required who had to know what their companions in other fields were doing. Security did not help any here as quite often a man was only allowed to know the details of his own small field of activities and had no idea of the work of his colleagues. It was useless for the electronic and aerodynamic experts to design a missile airframe which left an inadequate section for the rocket motor, or to mount delicate control equipment in the motor compartment, for example. Nor could the radio control hope to be effective unless such things as ionization in the rocket jet were allowed for. The many specialized fields of knowledge which go into the small space of a missile, needed the perfection of entirely new development techniques, such as systems engineering, and the use of electronic simulators which have now also found extensive use in other fields.

Essentially of what does a weapon system consist? Considering as an example the defence of the United Kingdom, which is, as mentioned earlier, a more difficult problem than that of the North American Continent where a much longer early warning can be obtained, the first essential is early warning radar.

This is limited by several factors so that it will only warn against the attack without divulging the magnitude of the raid or the specific target that is likely to be attacked. As many decoy raids will undoubtedly be made at the same time, it will be impossible during the early warning phase to decide which defence missiles must be prepared for firing. Accordingly a general alert is sounded at this stage. As far as Britain is concerned it would appear that completely inadequate radar defences are available over the European sector to give early warning. Only if an attack came over Western Germany would Britain have the period of warning which is needed. Attempts are of course being made to rectify these shortcomings.

The tactical control radar next picks up the attackers and the greater resolution enables an accurate appraisal of the situation to be made. The tactical radar is divided into sectors covering the whole defence perimeter and each sector examines critically all activity in its own area. Britain is extremely well organized for this type of defence. It will enable the third defensive stage to be put in operation, that is, interception.

A selective system, ideally a computer though often at present a human controller, decides which type of missile is going to be used, for example, air-to-air or surface-to-air, and makes the necessary arrangements for the firing. By carrying the missile closer to the attacker using an interceptor aircraft or by using a long-range surface-to-air missile, early defence is possible before the raiders reach the target area. But provision has also to be made for an inner ring of ground-to-air missiles to be alerted in case the attack penetrates the main defences. Obviously, with nuclear fusion bombs, interception must take place as far as possible from the target and, if practicable, over the sea. The final aspect of the defence system is concerned with the missile itself, its size, its payload, and its performance; what type of attacker it will have to contend with, and how best it should make its interception.

One might naturally inquire why go to all this trouble of making complex missiles and electronic brains when a piloted jet interceptor is such an efficient and fast machine? The fact is that if bombers are moving near sonic velocities at extreme altitudes there is very little time for interception to be made without subjecting the interceptor to high lateral accelerations. In addition the fighter has to be capable of a safe return with its human pilot, thereby further complicating the system. Moreover, the modern fighter aircraft is a highly complex machine and its pilot needs a tremendous amount of training. It is becoming more and more difficult to train sufficient numbers of pilots in the short time available and this will be impossibly difficult during any future war. By having an expendable missile, however, which can manœuvre extremely rapidly, interception becomes more certain. The penalty is, of course, that of having to make a guidance mechanism which no matter how complex it is will still lack the discrimination of the human pilot. But we cannot have it both ways. Human pilots are inadequate for the accelerations involved, nor are their reactions quick enough in many circumstances.[13] We put the discrimination therefore into the hands of ground controllers, letting them act as over-riders for the missile control but putting all the routine manœuvres in the circuits of the speedy—if not yet completely reliable—electronic pilots. It is possible to make as many missiles and their brains as needed within the production limits of a nation's economy and to regard them as being expendable, but there is a definite limit in human material for highly trained aircrews which cannot be regarded as expendable any longer.

As for the missile itself, this consists of three separate systems, the airframe, the propulsion unit, and the guidance.

Early missiles were modelled very much along the lines of conventional aircraft,[14] being merely a fuselage with normal wings having straight or swept-back leading edges, and a conventional type of tail plane. Such missiles suffered from the disadvantage that a turn had to be preceded by a bank. Modern missiles have pencil-slim bodies with cruciform wings and a cruciform tail surface mounted sometimes normally and sometimes in a tail-first configuration.[15] Many wings are rectangular in form, while a number have swept leading edges. The cruciform arrangement makes possible rapid manœuvring, either up-down or side-side, or combinations of motion in the two planes.[16]

The airframe itself has to be stable and not prone to break up under high lateral accelerations at up to Mach numbers where aerodynamic heating weakens structural materials. Quantitative manœuvres must be possible, for example, not just moving to the right, but move to the right at, say, 1·375 G's for 12 milli-seconds.

A typical series of trials for the development of a missile might first start with pure ballistic firings or wind-tunnel work on models. Having ascertained that the design is aerodynamically sound, a clockwork mechanism will be installed, and the missile will be equipped with a propulsion unit so that it can be put through a series of timer-controlled manœuvres. These might first be made only in the up/down plane, then side/side and finally in combinations of the two planes of freedom. Roll must be eliminated or these manœuvres become impossibly difficult. Roll stability of the missile is thus a factor which must be perfected in the early stages before it is programmed on manœuvres, otherwise pitch and yaw control become ineffective.

Having shown that the missile is aerodynamically stable and that the servomechanisms can give positive control at definite quantitutive rates in both pitch and yaw, the guidance mechanism can be incorporated. The missile will be fired to see how close it can approach to target drones, and finally it will be tested in a live firing with an explosive warhead.

The early missile development was made before supersonic wind tunnels were available. Test vehicles were then used. These were rocket powered, or even dropped models accelerated by gravity.

Some small models were fired in aeroballistic ranges. This procedure was both time consuming and expensive. The modern technique is to make extensive use of an electronic simulator, such as the analogue computer. In these instruments a continuously varying voltage is obtained from a potentiometer moved by a cam. The voltages represent such things as missile speed, orientation, aerodynamic constants, physical characteristics of the atmosphere, thrust of the motor, etc. All the parameters governing the performance of the missile are thus represented by voltages which vary between limits corresponding to the probable limits of those to be encountered during an actual flight. Tests which are made include the variation of the parameters in order to determine the sensitivity of the missile. Those parameters which most disturb the missile can then be studied in free flight. The great advantage of the simulator is that it gives an approximate solution quickly; but it must work in real time, that is the parameters must be varied in the same periods that the variations take place during the flight of a real missile. It also has the greatest advantage that parts of a real missile can be tested in a simulated missile. A servomechanism can, for example, be connected to the simulator as though it were assembled in a missile. This is especially useful when non-linear pieces of apparatus have to be tested because they cannot be simulated by the analogue method.

Missiles can be classed into the two broad sections of defensive and offensive weapons. Defensive missiles consist at present mainly of anti-aircraft devices, but the growing development of offensive missiles (*Fig.* 1.5) will make it necessary for the guided missile industry to produce some form of defence against missiles themselves.

Anti-aircraft devices can be air launched, when they are known as air-to-air missiles, or can be ground launched as surface-to-air weapons. Ground launched missiles usually employ a booster for the launching stage which can be mounted either in a tandem arrangement or as a wrap-around booster. Boosters are almost invariably solid-propellant rockets (*Fig.* 1.6), giving a high total impulse in a short period of time. The missile itself can be powered in several ways, by pulse-jet, turbo-jet, ramjet or rocket.

Surface-to-surface missiles are offensive weapons. They encompass both winged and unwinged vehicles, and the various means of propulsion. Winged vehicles often have a preliminary rocket boost, and the larger rocket vehicles must be in the form of multi-step rockets, often with a final winged stage for extreme ranges. Surface-to-surface missiles can be used tactically or strategically.

FIG. 1.5. *A number of strategic and tactical missiles are winged like the Chance Vought REGULUS shown here taking off on rocket boost from a mobile field launcher at the Naval Air Missile Test Centre, Pt. Mugu, California. This missile has also been launched successfully from warships and submarines.*

(Photo. Chance Vought Aircraft)

In the United States two systems of missile designation are currently in use. The Army and the Navy use the following letters: SAM, surface-to-air; AAM, air-to-air; ASM, air-to-surface; SSM, surface-to-surface; UAM, underwater-to-air; USM, underwater-to-surface; AUM, air-to-underwater, and SUM, surface-to-underwater, missiles. The prefix X indicates an experimental vehicle.

FIG. 1.6. *Tactical winged missiles are usually launched from zero-length mobile launchers by means of solid propellant rockets. This MATADOR is transported on the truck and in the firing position hydraulic devices raise the nose and tail of the missile so that it is correctly elevated. The jet engine is started and when it reaches full thrust the rocket boost is fired. Then the thrust is of sufficient magnitude to shear a retaining bolt and as the missile moves forward the forward support swings away so that it does not foul the booster.*

(Photo. Glenn L. Martin Co.)

The Air Force, on the other hand, use: TM, tactical missile; SM, strategic missile, and GAR, air-to-air; GAM, air-to-ground, missiles. Surface-to-air interceptors are designated IM.

Missiles are guided in many ways, usually the guidance system is based on radar devices of one kind or another, though some modern guidance systems rely upon inertial methods and natural frames of reference, so that they are immune to enemy interference.

Associated with the actual missiles there are test installations for guidance systems, test cells for the propulsion units and test vehicles for developing the whole missile. All these various sections will be discussed in more detail in subsequent chapters.

REFERENCES

[1] BURGESS, E., *The Engineer*, **184**, 1947, Oct. 3, 10, 17, 24, 31, 308 etc.
[2] PERRING, W. G. H., *Jnl. Royal Aero. Soc.*, **50**, 1946, 483.
[3] GATLAND, K. W., *Jnl. Brit. Int. Soc.*, **7**, 4, July 1948, 160–9.
[4] GARDNER, G. W. H., *Chartered Mechan. Engin.*, **2**, Jan. 1955, 5–22.
[5] ANON, *Amer. Aviation*, **18**, 11, Oct. 25 1954, 40–42, 46.
[6] BURGESS, E., *Rocket Propulsion*, Chapman & Hall 1954, Ch. VI.
[7] CARHART, R. C., *Aeronautical Engineering Review*, **12**, 2, Feb. 1953.
[8] SMITH, J. F., *Inter Avia*, **10**, 5, May 1955, 300–9.
[9] BRITISH *Government White Paper*, Feb. 1955, see *Aeroplane*, 10 May 1955, 658–60.
[10] *Financial Times*, London, 27 Jan. 1956, p 1.
[11] REYNOLDS, F. D., *Boeing Magazine*, **1**, 1953.
[12] EDITORIAL, *The Engineer*, 26 Nov. 1954.
[13] BYRNES, V. A., *Aeron. Engin. Review*, **12**, 4, Apr. 1953, 61 64, 70.
[14] BURGESS, E., loc. cit., 1.
[15] BONNEY, E. A., *Aero Digest*, **69**, 1, July 1954, 61, 62, 64.
[16] GARDNER, G. W. H., loc. cit., 4.

CHAPTER II

PROPULSION AND PROPELLANTS

◎

EXCEPT in the cases of the glider bomb and of the free falling guided bomb all guided missiles utilize a power plant or propulsion unit. There are indeed several methods of missile propulsion, each of which has its most convenient speed and altitude range. (*Fig.* 2.1.) These power plants can be conveniently divided into air-aspiring engines and air independent engines. In the former class are the simple pulse-jet, the turbo-jet and the pure ramjet. In the latter we have solid-propellant and liquid-propellant rockets.

The simple pulse-jet found operation during World War II in the FZG-76, popularly known as the buzz bomb or V-1 flying bomb.[1, 2] Essentially it consists of a duct closed at one end by flap valves. A combustible mixture within the duct is ignited by means of a spark plug. Heat released gives an expansion which results in ejection of the heated air and combustion products through the open end of the duct. Even when the pressure inside the duct has fallen to that of the surrounding atmosphere, the gases in the tail pipe possess momentum so that as they continue to move away from the chamber they leave a negative pressure within it. This allows a new cycle of fuel and air to be drawn in through the flap valves and fuel inlets, and the cycle repeats at a frequency dependent upon the resonance of the combustion chamber, ducts and valves. Usually it is of the order of 300 cycles per second and this gave the characteristic buzz to the German flying bombs.

After the first few explosions, the combustion of each succeeding cycle is initiated by the residual hot gases and high temperature parts. High combustion temperatures are permissible because the engine is intermittent in operation.

In the pulse-jet (*Fig.* 2.2) the thrust increases as a function of air speed because high air speeds give rise to increased ram pressure which in turn increases the combustion chamber pressure and hence

32

the thermal efficiency. Moreover, at high forward speeds more air is taken into the motor so that the mass passing through the engine in unit time is increased. As thrust depends upon mass flow there is accordingly an increased thrust due to this effect. This power plant obviates the expensive compressor and turbine of the turbo-jet. Pulse-jets will still deliver appreciable thrusts at low forward speeds

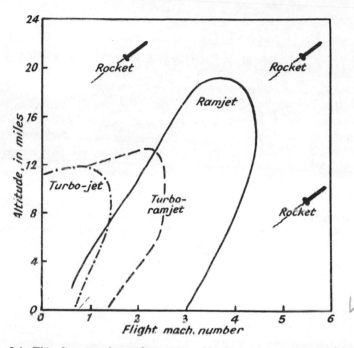

FIG. 2.1. *This diagram shows the ranges of both speed and altitude for the various types of missile power plants.*

and score over ramjets. Unfortunately they can only be used at relatively low speeds and consequently low efficiencies, but consume more fuel than do turbo-jets. In practical applications pulse-jets find use in target drones where a cheap expendable engine is required.

However, some target drones and, indeed, a number of subsonic missiles use turbo-jets (*Fig.* 2.3) as power plants. These have low specific propellant consumptions (of the order of 1 lb/lb hr) so that the missiles have long ranges. The inherent failing is, however, that

FIG. 2.2. *A pulse-jet engine was used in the German V-1 flying bomb, but such engines, although they have nowadays been considerably developed, are not used in operational missiles but only in target drones. This photograph shows a modern pulse-jet under test developing a thrust of* 120 *lb.*

(Photo. Saunders-Roe Ltd.)

FIG. 2.3. *Short life turbo-jets like this Viper unit find extensive use for drones and for subsonic winged missiles.*

(Photo. Armstrong Siddeley Ltd.)

the speed range and operating height are limited to those normally associated with the turbo-jet aircraft engine. The same applies, of course, to the pulse-jet. Turbo-jets for missiles are usually of a short-life variety, like the Armstrong Siddeley VIPER which was designed for use in the JINDIVIK target drone.[3] The greatly increased speed and the operating height of jet aircraft have presented an ever increasing problem to the ground defences who must have a certain number of live practices if they are to become efficient in the use of new anti-aircraft devices. The JINDIVIK was produced to provide a realistic target for such practice shoots and the VIPER is a compact propulsion unit of simple construction designed for cheapness in mass production. The first models gave a thrust of 1,640 lb (744 kg) but improved versions are now in production. A seven-stage axial compressor—which minimizes engine diameter—feeds the air into an annular combustion chamber, after which the hot gases expand through a single-stage turbine. The accessories are only two; a combined fuel and oil pump assembly, and a fuel flow control. Technical data of this unit are given in the Table 2.1.

TABLE 2,1   *Data on Typical Short-Life Turbo-Jet*

Static thrust	1,640 lb	740 kg
Dry weight	365 lb	165 kg
Max. diameter	23·25 in	59 cm
Overall length	65·4 in	166 cm
Specific fuel consumption	1·09 lb/hr/lb	kg/hr/kg
Static air mass flow	30 lb/sec	14 kg/sec

The next stage in the speed and altitude range of missile power plants is covered by the ramjet. The idea of the ramjet or athodyd is by no means new.[4] Proposals and patents have been appearing for many years. Essentially the ramjet is a stage between the turbo-jet and the rocket. Its great advantage over the former is that it can operate successfully over a supersonic range of velocities. Moreover, the absence of turbine blades permits higher working temperatures so that a richer fuel/air ratio can be employed. The result is increased thrust. Compared with the rocket it has the great advantage that oxygen can be taken from the atmosphere in order to support combustion so that the additional weight of an oxidant is avoided. This latter fact can also, sometimes, be a disadvantage, because it necessarily limits the ceiling of the ramjet. In some designs an attempt has been made to give higher ceilings by carrying an oxidant for use when the ram air fails to bring sufficient oxygen into the combustion chamber. A ramjet operates on a cycle which is basically similar to that of other air-aspiring engines; compression, combustion, expansion.[5] Compression is achieved by slowing down the air stream which is entering the duct, and consequently, in order to obtain good compression, ramjets must travel at high air speeds. Since 1946 NACA experiments have extended the speed range of ramjets from subsonic to Mach 3·5* in their tests.[6] Above this range the problems of aerodynamic heating become serious so that attempts are now being made to study basic methods of overcoming them. Preliminary studies were made with rocket-propelled models at Mach 5. At this speed the temperature rise in the boundary layer is to as much as 870° C.

Also active in the ramjet field are the Marquardt Aircraft Company and the Curtiss-Wright Corporation in the United States and the Bristol Aeroplane Company and Napier in the United Kingdom. (*Fig.* 2.4.) A Bristol ramjet now in production is the THOR which has powered more than 200 test vehicles to heights well above 50,000 ft (16,500 m) and to the limits of the Woomera range at high supersonic speeds.

Rocket boost is often employed to accelerate the ramjet to its operating speed. Although this power plant can operate at both subsonic and supersonic velocities, the supersonic ramjet will find most use in missile propulsion, turbo-jets or pulse-jets being preferable for subsonic applications. Essentially the ramjet has the components shown in *Fig.* 2.5. It consists of a diffuser which comprises a subsonic and a supersonic section, a combustion chamber with flame holders, and an expansion nozzle.

With supersonic ramjets it is found that the most efficient method of compression is to have a series of shocks, first oblique and then normal.[7] For high Mach numbers an isentropic spike inlet provides the oblique shock or series of shocks,[8] while a simple diverging channel, which must not permit separation or turbulence provides the subsonic diffuser. The design of the diffuser is governed by the

---

*Mach number is the relation between the velocity of the moving body and the velocity of sound in the surrounding air.

(a) *A test vehicle developed by Napier and propelled by a supersonic ramjet power plant. The vehicle is launched by means of eight solid-propellant booster rockets, the wrap-around configuration of which is clearly shown.*

(Photo. D. Napier & Son Ltd.)

(b) *At launching the boosters are seen accelerating the vehicle to a speed at which it can operate solely under ramjet power. They are then automatically jettisoned.*

(Photo. Crown copyright reserved, reproduced by permission of the Controller, H.M. Stationery Office)

FIG. 2.4

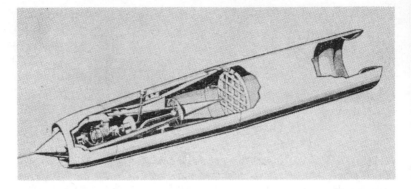

FIG. 2.5. *Moving into the higher speed and altitude range, missiles are using supersonic ramjets. This drawing shows a typical supersonic ramjet. At the left the cone-shaped device at the front is the diffuser in which are also housed such accessories as the fuel pump and the fuel control. A ring-shaped fuel injector is mounted near the end of the diffuser and farther downstream is the grid-shaped flame holder. The supersonic exhaust nozzle is shown cut away at the right of the unit.*

(Courtesy, Marquardt Aircraft Co.)

Mach number of the vehicle, and if the ramjet is not travelling at its design speed, the normal shock may move forward out of, or may retreat into the subsonic diffuser. If it interferes with the oblique shock, a rapid falling off in efficiency takes place. The ramjet has been described as a narrow-band engine. Variations from the designed speed and the altitude range require compensating changes in the engine itself.

NACA has developed a means of controlling the normal shock so that it remains in its correct position close to the inlet.[9] The system uses a pressure-sensitive device positioned in the diffuser about where the shock should be. If the shock wave moves backwards the fuel supply is increased and the effect is to move the shock forward. If, on the other hand, the shock is advancing past the sensing device, the fuel supply is reduced so that it will return the shock to its correct position. Tests have shown that this method of control operates quite satisfactorily over wide ranges of speed, ambient air-pressure, and angles of attack. Power for driving fuel-feed systems in ramjets can be obtained either from inert gas pressure or by means of a fuel pump driven by ram air.

The main problem in the ramjet combustion chamber is the holding of the flame, and this is done by means of 'can' and 'gutter' type flame holders.[10] These stabilize the flame front in the neighbourhood of a solid surface immersed in the flowing gases. The efficiency of the power plant is governed by the mixture ratio, the velocity of the air entering the chamber from the diffuser, the pressure and stagnation temperature of the ambient air. Efficiency increases with increased pressures, up to a point with richer mixtures, and also with reduced ambient temperatures, that is at higher altitudes. High frequency combustion instability is also a problem and can lead to the destruction of the burners and the flame holders. Special probe instrumentations developed by NACA scientists have enabled them to investigate the mechanism of these instabilities and to evolve new design features in recent engines which have overcome instability defects.

Nozzles can be just straight tubes, but are normally convergent/divergent pipes in order to give choking and to produce supersonic velocities at discharge pressures similar to ambient pressures. The length of the exhaust nozzle should be as short as possible in order to minimize weight and drag, but the divergence angle has to be limited in order to keep the non-axial momentum of the exhaust gases as low as possible and to avoid flow separation.

Some manufacturers of ramjets claim that they are the perfect power source for medium and long-range guided missiles and pilotless aircraft and for short-range guided missiles launched from supersonic platforms.

Their claims are based on the facts that at speeds in excess of twice that of sound the ramjet gives the highest thrust-to-weight ratio, lower fuel consumption, lowest development costs, lowest production costs, and in addition no moving parts contact the burning gases. No compressors nor turbines are needed and the fuel controls and the fuel pumps are housed outside of the propulsive duct.

A supersonic ramjet may obtain a compression ratio of up to 40 : 1 and, in addition, ramjets can use colloidal solutions of solid fuels, for example light metals, in the normal jet fuel. This can result in tremendous improvements in the amount of thrust derived per pound of fuel consumed. These improved fuels lead to high operating temperatures. In point of fact present-day high-power ramjets give rise to temperatures of up to 2,180°C and it has been necessary to use special alloys with cobalt and nickel to give combustion chambers and nozzles which are capable of withstanding them. The fact that a ramjet propulsion plant has no moving parts in contact with the high temperature combustion gases is very important as far as reliability is concerned. In subsequent chapters it will be stressed that reliability of each component part of a missile is most important. This is because most missiles can be regarded as being a system of components in series so that the failure of one of these leads to a failure of the missile as a whole.

The first successful flight of a supersonic ramjet in the United States took place in June 1945, being that of a 6 in (15·24 cm) diameter ramjet developed by the Applied Physics Laboratory of the Johns Hopkins University. (*Fig.* 2.6.) Ramjets were later used in

FIG. 2.6. *A large ramjet test vehicle is launched from the Naval Ordnance Test Station, Inyokern, California. Its velocity was far into the supersonic range and it was developed for the U.S. Navy Bureau of Ordnance by the Applied Physics Laboratory of the Johns Hopkins University. The cloud of smoke arises from the burning of a large solid-propellant booster rocket needed to bring the ramjet to its operating flight speed.*

(Photo. Applied Physics Lab., Johns Hopkins University/Navy) the GORGON, LARK and GAPA test vehicles, and ramjet engines are known to be employed on several modern missiles. Two Marquardt units power the BOMARC IM-99 surface-to-air missile and they are assisted by an Aerojet rocket engine for take-off. RIGEL, developed by Grumman Aircraft, is a ramjet-powered Navy missile of long range. Bendix TALOS and the North American NAVAHO also use advanced ramjets, while some unnamed British missiles are known to be ramjet powered.

The use of ramjets instead of pure rockets gives the missile a longer range because of reduced propellant consumption. Interception can take place at great distances from the target, a big advantage if atomic weapons are being used in the attack.

For the highest speed ranges and greatest altitudes the rocket (*Fig.* 2.7) has become an essential means of missile propulsion. It is indeed used as the main propulsion unit in many missiles and for most missiles it forms the booster. (*Fig.* 2.8.) The rocket is best defined as a device which produces a propulsive jet from material originally carried within itself. Accordingly it differs from other power plants in that it operates independently of the surrounding medium and can, therefore, be used at extreme altitudes where other propulsive systems would be starved of the oxygen which they need for combustion. The rocket can operate in the vacuum of interplanetary space and is most efficient where its exhaust is discharging into a vacuum.[11]

Rockets may be divided into two broad classes, those deriving their energy from the combustion of solid propellants, and those which rely on one or more liquids as energy carriers for the acceleration of the mass of the propellants in the form of a propulsive jet. Further sub-divisions are possible but are not necessary for the purpose of this book.

The operation of a rocket depends upon the release of heat energy by the propellants. The ideal propellant should release the maximum amount of available heat into combustion products which should have the lowest possible mean molecular weight. Acceleration of the working fluid—the gases evolved from the combustion of the propellants—takes place by means of a convergent/divergent expansion nozzle which is able to produce supersonic flow. The thrust developed by the rocket motor is given ideally by the product of mass flow and exhaust velocity. In practice nozzles do not expand

(a) A solid propellant rocket motor under test. (Photo. Thiokol Chemical Corp)

(b) A liquid propellant guided missile rocket motor under static test showing
shockwaves.   (Photo. Sir W. G. Armstrong Whitworth Aircraft)

Fig. 2.7

FIG. 2.8. *The solid propellant booster rocket used to achieve zero-length launching with the Martin Matador.*

(Photo. U.S. Information Services)

the exhaust to ambient pressure, and the thrust consists of the sum of two components, one being the momentum thrust and the other arising from the pressure differential between the discharging gases at the lip of the nozzle and the ambient air. It is the former which is the product of mass flow and jet velocity, while the latter is the product of nozzle mouth area and the pressure differential. It should be noted that this latter can have a negative value if the nozzle over expands. A given number of pounds per square inch over expansion is more detrimental to overall performance than is the same number of pounds per square inch under expansion.[12, 13]

Maximum thrust for a given propellant and for a given chamber pressure is obtained when the pressure term in the thrust equation is zero. That is, when the nozzle expands the gases to atmospheric pressure. In practice this cannot be achieved because the rocket passes through a large range of ambient pressure values during its flight. Moreover it is found that if a rocket nozzle is designed to give complete expansion at high altitudes, the weight penalty from the increased size of the nozzle more than offsets any gain resulting from the improved performance of a higher jet velocity.[14]

The jet velocity of a rocket depends primarily upon the temperature inside the combustion chamber and the molecular weight of the exhaust gases. It also varies with the expansion ratio and the ratio of specific heats of the combustion products, but the first two variables are the more important. The highest possible jet velocity should be obtained in order to reduce for a given mission the proportion of the rocket which has to consist originally of propellants.

It is often more convenient to use the term 'specific impulse' rather than that of jet velocity. Specific impulse is the jet velocity divided by 'g' and has the dimensions of time. It is often expressed, however, as a specific thrust, that is the thrust developed for a unit weight of the propellants ejected per second. An example is 250 lb thrust per lb propellant per sec, or 250 sec.*

The specific propellant consumption is the reciprocal of the specific thrust and is, naturally, high in rocket engines compared with other prime movers because of the weight of oxidant which has to be included in its calculation. (Table 2.2.)

TABLE 2.2   *Specific Fuel/Propellant Consumption of Power Plants as a Function of Mach Number*

Type	lb/lb hr at a Mach Number of:			
	1	2	3	4
Pulse-jet	1	—	—	—
Turbo-jet†	1	2	4	—
Ramjet	8	3	3	3
Rocket	18	18	18	18

† Assumes an afterburner beyond Mach 1·5.

As far as the design of a complete missile or rocket vehicle is concerned, it is sometimes more convenient to refer to the density impulse which is the product of the specific impulse and the mean specific gravity of the propellants. Values of these parameters are given in Table 2.3 for some propellant combinations. It will be noted

*References to the thrusts of power plants made throughout this book are in pounds or kilograms weight.

TABLE 2.3   Comparisons of Liquid Propellant Combinations

Oxidizer	Fuel	Mixture ratio	S.I. (sec)	Temp. °C	Density impulse
H_2O_2	—	—	110	480	150
	octane	5·1 : 1	230	2,200	275
	hydrazine	1·4 : 1	280	2,400	347
Liquid oxygen	hydrogen	4·0 : 1	375	2,700	118
	octane	2·2 : 1	248	3,000	238
	ethanol	1·5 : 1	230	2,900	225
	gasoline	2·5 : 1	242	2,950	235
	hydrazine	0·5 : 1	259	2,400	272
Nitric acid	octane	4·0 : 1	220	2,600	280
	aniline	3·0 : 1	215	2,800	295
Nitromethane	—	—	210	2,250	240

that these values of specific impulse fall short of those often quoted in the older references. This is because dissociation reduces the heat yield and, in addition, non-stoichiometric mixtures have often to be used to reduce burning temperatures to values compatible with present-day materials and cooling techniques.

Rocket motors can now be made to operate as efficiently as other heat engines and considerable developments are expected in the coming years.

Solid-propellant rockets are the oldest and the most simple. They do not require separate tanks, propellant lines or pumps, because all the propellant is contained within the combustion chamber. Solid-propellant rockets are sub-divided into two main classes, (a) unrestricted burning rockets and (b) restricted burning rockets.

The former type gives higher thrusts and total impulses—product of thrust by duration of burning—and are employed for artillery projectiles, air-to-air, air-to-ground, ground-to-air and ground-to-ground missiles, and for missile boosters. The propellant is in the form of sticks which are known as grains or charges, the size and geometry of which control the thrust programme. Burning always takes place on the surface of the charge, the propellant burning to gaseous products which escape and leave fresh surfaces for further reaction to take place. The speed of the reaction depends upon the rate at which heat is transferred to the propellant surface and this is affected by, among other things, the temperature of the propellant and ambient temperature.[15] As the burning rate should be controllable, this ambient temperature sensitivity is a decided disadvantage. A rocket which operates satisfactorily in the tropics may have a considerable diminution of thrust if stored and fired in arctic conditions or at high altitudes. Two methods of attacking the problem are possible. The storage of the unit in temperature-controlled magazines or the development of propellants which are insensitive to temperature changes as normally encountered in operational service. A number of modern propellants have been perfected which permit efficient operation over a temperature range from tropical to polar conditions. Large solid-propellant rockets need to be maintained at a constant temperature for constant performance. The HONEST JOHN is kept warm during transport and before firing by an electric blanket wrapped around the missile.

By coating some of the exposed propellant surface with a burning inhibitor a restricted burning rocket is produced. This burns its propellant charge from one end to the other like a cigarette. Restricted burning rockets generally have smaller thrusts than the other type, but these thrusts last for a longer duration of time. Accordingly the second type of solid-propellant rocket finds application for the assisted take-off of aircraft, for missile power plants and sometimes for missile and ramjet boosters. A typical restricted burning unit is the Aerojet 14AS-1,000 which produces approximately 1,000 lb (454 kg) of thrust for a period of 14 sec and is capable of being recharged and used a number of times.

Most modern rocket propellants are developed from smokeless powders containing nitroglycerin and nitrocellulose; they are known as double-base propellants.[16] They may give a specific impulse in the region of 200 sec and develop a temperature of 2,700° C. The charge is designed to retain good mechanical properties under extremes of temperature, stress and acceleration, and to produce the minimum amount of smoke.

The standard British cordite which was used for rocket propellants in the thousands of unguided missiles, consisted of nitroglycerin, nitrocellulose and carbamite (diethyl diphenyl urea) in the proportions 50 : 41 : 9 parts by weights respectively.[17] Other propellants have been manufactured from solid ingredients in a plasticizing binder. An example of this type is the GALCIT propellant which consisted of finely divided potassium perchlorate in asphalt and oil[18] and which has the decided advantage of being easily filled in any size of rocket tube. Such propellants as these are very useful for restricted burning rockets as they do not crack from the inhibitor or from the chamber walls. Charges as large as 4 ft (1·22 m) in length and 2 ft (0·6 m) in diameter have been cast experimentally. Total impulses of 500,000 lb sec (227,000 kg sec) have been obtained. Examples of a number of solid propellants are given in Table 2.4.

TABLE 2.4   *Composition of some Solid Propellants*

	WASAG R61	BAKA	GALCIT	NDRC	Cordite
Nitrocellulose	61·5	59·9			41
Diethylene glycol dinitrate	34·0				
Ethyl phenyl urethane	1·4				
Diphenyl urethane	2·1				
Nitroglycerin		26·9			50
Potassium sulphate		2·9			
Ethyl centralite		2·9			
Alphanitronapthalene		6·1			
Potassium perchlorate			75·0		
Asphalt and oil			25·0		
Ammonium picrate				45	
Sodium nitrate				45	
Resin binder				10	
Diethyl diphenyl urea					9
Specific impulse (sec.)	182	150	180	180	190

Note: compositions are by weight per cent.

The great advantage of the solid-propellant rocket is its high total impulse to total weight ratio and also its reliability. The operation of such rockets may, however, be more costly than their liquid-propellant counterpart. Solid-propellant rockets can have a programmed thrust.[19] This is achieved by a suitable moulding of the grain or charge; concentric holes of gear, star, or other shapes being able to give controlled thrust changes during the burning of the solid-propellant rocket, thus making it a more versatile power plant.

The Thiokol Chemical Corporation has announced work on new

low-cost solid propellants for guided missiles, rocket assisted take-off and boosters. A static test of one of these units is shown in *Fig.* 2.7. The greatest use of solid-propellant rocket units, in addition to unguided missiles, is for booster work with liquid-propellant rockets and with ramjets, and for the assisted take-off of pilotless aircraft like the REGULUS and the MATADOR. Data concerning the solid-propellant units are given in Table 2.5.

TABLE 2.5   *Data on Solid-Propellant Units*

Unit	BAKA	AEROJET 14AS-1,000	WASAG 109-522	TINY TIM
Propellant	Double base	Plastic	Diglycol	Ballistite
Thrust (lb)	1,760	1,000	4,410	30,000
Specific impulse (sec)	150	180	182	188
Propellant consumption (lb/sec)	12·5	5·9	25	160
Dimensions (inches)				
length	72	35·4	47·6	123
max. diameter	10	10·25	11·3	11·75
Weight (lb)				
full	260	205	203	760
dry	160	120	128	140
Firing time (sec)	8	14·5	3	1

During the last twenty years the liquid-propellant experimental units have been developed into respectable power plants for missiles and engines for aircraft.[20] (*Figs.* 2.9 and 2.10.) Indeed some rocket engines nowadays develop millions of horsepower. These propellants are fed under pressure from tanks to a separate combustion chamber in which they are burned. Early rocket units were fed from pressurized tanks. Nowadays this feed system is only used for rockets which have a restricted period of burning and small total propellant consumption. Examples are found in some missiles and in assisted take-off units. Propellants can consist of two liquids (bi-propellants) and these can be self-igniting or non-self-igniting, one liquid (mono-propellant), or a combination of a liquid and a solid. It is also reported that some successful firings of rockets using bi-propellant systems have been made in which aluminium powder was suspended in one of the liquids to give a greater heat yield. Examples of some liquid-propellant units are given in Table 2.6.

For longer burning times and greater propellant consumptions pump feeds become necessary and are obtained by means of meshed gear or centrifugal pumps. A rough estimate of the point where the weight of the pumping system becomes less than the weight of the heavy tanks needed for tank pressurization is obtained when the rocket gives a total impulse of about 200,000 lb sec (90,000 kg sec).

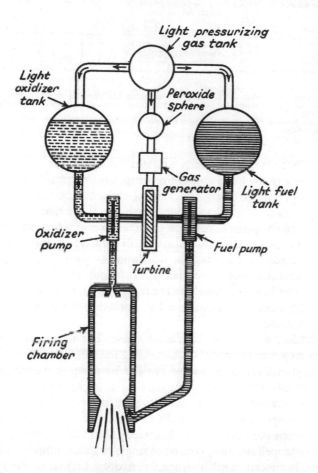

FIG. 2.9. *Diagram of a typical liquid-propellant rocket engine using a turbo-pump feed. Engines of this nature are needed for the larger rocket missiles.*

(Courtesy Ryan Aeronautical Co.)

TABLE 2.6   *Data on Liquid Propellant Units*

	Oxidizer	Fuel	Thrust (lb)	S.I. (sec)	Propellant consumption (lb/sec)	Overall length (in)	Maximum diameter (in)	Dry weight (lb)	Firing time (sec)
Walter 109-500	H_2O_2	—	1,103	103	10	57	27	260	30
Walter 109-509	H_2O_2	C	4,400	179	19·8	100	36	415	240+
WAC-Corporal	RFNA	Aniline]	1,500	193	7·8	11*	5¼*	50*	45
Snarler	LOX	Methanol	2,000	200	10	23*	12¼*	166	180+
Sprite	H_2O_2	—	5,000	100	23	84	20	350	16
Super Sprite	H_2O_2	Kerosene	4,200	150	21	117¼	20¼	600	40
Beta	H_2O_2	C	1,800	197	10·15	47	18	223	44
RMI 6,000	LOX	Ethanol	6,000	202	29·5	56	19	210	240+
Veronique	RFNA	Gasolene	9,000	204	44	—	—	—	36
RMI Viking	LOX	Ethanol	20,000	190	106	40*	16*	—	75

Notes:
*Refers to combustion chamber only.
The data are not complete on the Viking and Veronique. The Viking dry weight including pumps, fuel tanks and other structure, but excluding payload, amounts to about 2,000 lb and the Veronique about 290 lb.
C-fuel is a mixture of hydrazine hydrate and methanol, methanol is usually diluted with 25 to 35 per cent water.

In fact these pump-fed units are usually employed in long-range missiles where the large amount of propellant required could not be stored in pressurized tanks because of weight limitations.

Pump design has its attendant problems;[21] compatibility of the materials of the pumps, rotating parts, seals and lubricants with the propellants being vital. An example of trouble in this connexion was illustrated in the SNARLER development when the failure of a bearing allowed metal surfaces to rub and produce aluminium powder. The heat produced by the friction within the oxygen pump ignited the aluminium powder which burned in the oxygen and produced an explosion.[22]

Cavitation at the high operating speeds has to be prevented by booster stages or by slightly pressurizing the storage tanks.[23] Vapour locks in stop/start units can be avoided by priming systems and by vapour bleeds. Beyond an operating time of ten seconds or so, turbo-pump rockets can be shown to be lighter per pound of thrust than are solid-propellant rockets, and to be better than liquid-pressurized rockets when the operating time exceeds about 20–25 sec.

Mono-propellants may consist of single or mixed liquids. A typical example is concentrated hydrogen peroxide—known in England as H.T.P. (high test peroxide)—which is decomposed catalytically in a 'combustion' chamber. It was used in units such as the Walter 109-500 and in the De Havilland SPRITE. A mixture of two liquids,

Fig. 2.10. *The rocket motor for a modern missile. This liquid propellant unit is the Napier NRE.17 which uses high test peroxide and is probably used to propel one of the English Electric surface-to-air missiles. Note the cast injector head and machined combustion chamber and nozzle and also the compact arrangement of the propellant control valves attached to the head of the combustion chamber.* (Photo. D. Napier & Son Ltd.)

75 per cent methyl nitrate and 25 per cent methanol, formed the German mono-propellant Myrol. A suggested mono-propellant is propyl nitrate which is resistant to thermal effects and shock.[24]

Nitromethane is a promising mono-propellant, which has a low flame temperature. But it needs addition of oxygen for stable burning at low pressures although it burns smoothly at 35 atmospheres. The danger with this liquid is that it is explosive and that detonation can sweep back through the injectors and feed lines to the main tanks with disastrous results. On the other hand, the great advantage of a mono-propellant is that it halves the number of pumps, feed lines, valves, injectors, and storage tanks in the missile, and the fuelling facilities, bowsers etc., at the launching base. Suitable stabilizers are now doubtless being developed which will allow mono-propellants to be used in missiles.

Bi-propellants which are non-self-igniting, such as liquid oxygen and alcohol, need either some kind of pyrotechnic lighting torch for one shot devices, or an electrically ignited pre-ignition chamber for on/off operation.

Two sets of conditions apply for the choice of fuel and oxidizer. In the case of research vehicles the most advantageous mixture can be chosen regardless of cost or availability. For general or service use, however, liquids must be chosen which are non-toxic, are generally available or easily transportable to launching sites or airfields throughout the world, and should be produced at low cost from materials which will not be in short supply should an emergency arise.

Liquid oxygen is perhaps the best choice of oxidizer in these respects. It can be produced anywhere from the Earth's atmosphere by means of portable units which need only an electrical or other power supply. In large industrial centres the liquid is usually available at the rate of many tons per day and at a cost of about £15 per ton.[25] The disadvantage with this oxidizer is that of evaporation loss and while it has good corrosion properties and produces higher specific impulses than other propellants, it has the effect of giving to the propellant combination a low density impulse.

Nitric acid is also in plentiful supply but costs rather more than liquid oxygen—about £25 a ton[26]—while it has both good impulse and density ratings. Unfortunately it is highly corrosive and gives rise to toxic vapours. It can be safely stored in stainless steel

TABLE 2.7   *Examples of Rocket Propellant Combinations*

Oxidizer	Fuel	Type	Used in
Liquid oxygen	Alcohol	Non-self-igniting	V-2, 'Snarler', RMI 6,000, Viking
Nitric acid	Gasoline	Non-self-igniting	Veronique
	Aniline	Self-igniting	WAC-Corporal, Aerobee, Nike
Hydrogen peroxide	—	Mono-propellant	109-500, 'Sprite'
	Hydrazine hydrate + methanol	Self-igniting	109-509, Fairey 'Beta'
	Kerosene	Self-igniting when HTP is first catalysed	Super 'Sprite'

tanks and this is a very important property for defence missiles which may have to be loaded with propellants ready for an emergency. In the case of liquid oxygen it was found that the V-2s fuelled for more than an hour before firing showed a marked increase of failures from 35 to 61 per cent.[27] However, it is reported that some modern rocket motors have valves and pumps which are so designed that starts can be made without trouble even when the tanks have remained charged with liquid oxygen for some considerable time.[28] The high density of nitric acid makes it possible to have compact missiles with good performance, and while there are no reports of British units a large number of American missile motors operate with this oxidizer.

Concentrated hydrogen peroxide is a convenient oxidizer although at present it is rather expensive, at least £150 a ton.[29] It can, moreover, be used as a mono-propellant and for driving pump turbines. Storage and handling is rated mid-way between that of nitric acid and liquid oxygen if scrupulous cleanliness is observed in the tanks and the handling gear. It has a good density impulse rating.

Comparisons of the three standard oxidizers are given in Table 2.8.

Nearly all fuels will burn quite well with any oxidizer. Obviously aviation kerosene would be an ideal fuel as far as supply is concerned. However, the fuel of a rocket often has to serve as a coolant for the liquid-propellant motor, and that calls for a high specific heat and good thermal conductivity. Kerosene fails in these respects, alcohol is preferable as a coolant and finds extensive use in rocket

TABLE 2.8   *Comparison of Oxidizers*

	RFNA	Liquid oxygen	Nitro-methane	H_2O_2	Nitrogen tetroxide
Boiling point °C	154	−183	101	144	21
Vapour pressure mm Hg at 5° C	129	49·73 atm at BP	9·0	0·6	2 atm 35° C
Specific gravity	1·52	1·14	1·14	1·34	1·45
Corrosion	Severe	Good	Good	Reasonable	Good
Materials	Stainless steel	Stainless steel	Stainless steel	Stainless steel	Stainless steel
	Aluminium	Aluminium	Aluminium	Aluminium	Aluminium
	Teflon	Copper	Bakelite	Tin	Carbon steel
	Glass	Brass	Glass	Teflon	
		Bronze		Polythene	
		Monel		P.v.c.	Glass
		Rubber		Glass	
		Glass			

engines, especially in the form of 75 per cent methanol mixed with 25 per cent water to reduce the combustion chamber temperatures. Other fuels are legion but a comparison of some of the more common ones is given in Table 2.3.

Fuels should be chosen which are easily handled and which permit fuel containers, diaphragms, and expeller bags to resist corrosion and extremes of temperature.

Problems encountered in the combustion chamber include ignition delay, heat transfer and instability of combustion. Ignition delay is overcome by the use of injectors which are designed to reduce it to a minimum. The build up of propellants in the chamber prior to ignition, or of one propellant before the other is injected, results in hard starts which can shatter the rocket engine. Special control valves, operating in pre-determined and unalterable sequence, ensure that this cannot happen in modern missiles.

Heat transfer in a rocket motor is extremely high,[30] especially in the region of the nozzle throat. The protection of the motor walls consists of establishing a cool boundary layer by means of transpiration cooling—the injection of coolant through a porous chamber wall—or by film cooling which is obtained by injection of coolant through a series of orifices placed at strategic positions in the walls. These methods are normally employed in conjunction with regenerative cooling whereby one of the propellants is circulated in a helical path along the outside of the wall of the combustion chamber. The most critical conditions are experienced at the nozzle throat and coolant flow has there to be the greatest.

With regenerative motors the inner wall has to be thin in order to allow efficient transfer of heat to the coolant without having a large temperature gradient through the wall which would give rise to unacceptable temperatures on the inner wall surface.

Any build up of pressure from boiling coolant at the end of a run could cause the wall to fail. Accordingly, with stop/start devices, it is usual to provide a scavenge valve to exhaust the coolant from the coolant space at the end of each burning period.

Materials for combustion chamber and nozzle are usually conventional unless they come into contact with very hot reactive gases.[31] Then materials of high thermal conductivity and high strength characteristics at elevated temperatures are required. Unfortunately such materials are not readily available. Stainless steels are excellent from the latter standpoint but poor from the former, while aluminium and copper have good conductivity but poor strength at high temperatures. Compromises have to be made. Typical materials used are aluminium alloys, low carbon steel, alloy steels and mild steels chromium plated. The Germans had developed unique machines which could weld the combustion chamber for a V-2 rocket in twenty minutes.

The chamber weight for a given rocket motor is directly proportional to the thrust, while the nozzle weight increases as the 3/2 power of the thrust. The consequence is that larger motors will have to have large and heavy nozzles. There is no doubt that large rocket motors will be needed for long-range rockets and methods have to be employed to keep down the overall engine weight. One method is to use multiple nozzles, another is to sub-divide the large rocket motor into a number of smaller units. This latter method is very useful in that it permits throttling of a rocket unit without operating the injectors and the motor inefficiently. In modern rocket construction the trend seems to be to eliminate heavy castings with bolted flanges etc., and to use instead welded construction as in the V-2. This results in lighter motors.

Thermal stresses are set up in rocket motors, and expansion joints must be incorporated in large units. Especially to be avoided are distortions of the coolant passage and of the injectors. The former could give rise to local flow anomalies which would produce hot spots and motor burn-out while the latter can lead to instability.

The efficient operation of the rocket motor depends as much as anything upon the injectors. When the liquid propellants are injected the reaction begins almost immediately on the interface between the two liquids which evaporate rapidly because of the heat generated.[32] By using suitable absorption spectroscopic characteristics the combustion may be improved. This might be done by introducing dye-stuff into the propellant liquids. The reaction is completed in the vapour phase at a pressure of about 30 atmospheres and at temperatures ranging from 2,000 to 2,700° C. These combustion temperatures are hotter than anything experienced in all ordinary furnaces. The temperature patterns are important matters for investigation because these determine where film cooling injectors should be situated. They are investigated with movable probes and, in addition, gas samples are extracted for analysis with radio-frequency mass spectrometers to determine combustion processes. Spectroscopic studies of absorption bands help to determine temperatures within the chamber.

Injectors have, therefore, to ensure rapid mixing and atomization of the propellants in order to give smooth combustion. There are many different types, some of which are better suited to certain propellants than are others. One function of the injector is to safeguard combustion stability. Oscillations can be over a wide range of frequencies[33] and can be most destructive. The design of injector and the geometry of the combustion chamber and feed lines can obviate instability for definite operating conditions. Sometimes, however, the thrust of a single rocket unit has to be variable and certain thrust values can cause instable operation. In that case it has been shown by Tsien[34] and by Marble and Cox[35] that a feed-back servo control, sensing the changes in pressure and operating changes in propellant delivery, can damp out the oscillations and give smooth combustion.

REFERENCES

[1] EDELMAN, L. B., *S.A.E. Reprint*, Nat. Aeron. Meeting, Los Angeles, 3–5 October, 1946.
[2] MANILDI, F. F., *S.A.E. Reprint*, So. California Meeting, 19 April 1946.
[3] ARMSTRONG SIDDELEY MOTORS LTD., Press Release.
[4] SMITH, C. G., *Gas Turbines & Jet Propulsion For Aircraft*, Flight Publishing Co., London, 1947.

[5] AVERY, W. H., *Jet Propulsion*, **25**, 11, Nov. 1955, 604–14.
[6] NACA INSPECTION, Lewis Flight Propulsion Lab., 1954, p. 10.
[7] CLAUSER, F. H., *Jet Propulsion*, **24**, 2, March–Apr. 1954, 79–84, 94.
[8] MARSH, B. W., SEARS, G. A., *Jet Propulsion*, **24**, 3, May–June 1954, 155–61.
[9] NACA INSPECTION, loc. cit., 6, p. 11.
[10] MARSH, B. W., SEARS, G. A., loc. cit., 8.
[11] BURGESS, E., *Rocket Propulsion*, Chapman & Hall Ltd., London, 1954, Ch. I.
[12] STODOLA, A., *Steam & Gas Turbines*, McGraw Hill Book Co. Inc., New York, 1927.
[13] DIPLOCK, B. R., LOFTS, D. L., GRIMSTON, R.A., *Jnl. Royal Aero. Soc.*, **57**, Jan. 1953, 19–28.
[14] SMITH, E. T. B., *Jnl. Brit. Int. Soc.*, **12**, 2, March 1953, 53–62.
[15] BURGESS, E., *Aeronautics*, **18**, 6, May 1948, 38–50.
[16] BURGESS, E., *Rocket Propulsion*, Chapman & Hall Ltd., London, 1954, Ch. II.
[17] WHEELER, W. H., WHITTAKER, M., PIKE, H. H. M., *Jnl. Inst. of Fuel*, **20**, 1947, 137–56, 159.
[18] GALCIT Report, *Jnl. Brit. Int. Soc.*, **6**, 2, Sept. 1946, 34 61.
[19] SEIFERT, H. S., *Jet Propulsion*, **25**, 11, Nov. 1955, 594–603.
[20] DIPLOCK, B. R., *et al.*, loc. cit., 13.
[21] ROSS, C. C., *Aero Digest*, **63**, 3, Sept. 1954, 70, 72, 74, etc.
[22] HURDEN, D., *Jnl. Brit. Int. Soc.*, **14**, 4, July–Aug. 1955, 215–29.
[23] HURDEN, D., *Jnl. Brit. Int. Soc.*, **11**, 3, May 1952, 101–16.
[24] ETHYL CORPORATION, *Data Sheet*, New York, Sept. 1953.
[25] ALLEN, S., *Jnl. Brit. Int. Soc.*, **14**, 3, May–June, 1955, 165–8.
[26] ANON, *Aeroplane*, **87**, 6 Aug. 1954, 187–8.
[27] GREEN, C. F., Proc. Gass. Committee, *Rocket Exploration of the Upper Atmosphere*, Pergamon Press, London, 1954.
[28] HURDEN, D., loc. cit. 22.
[29] SLATER, A. E., *Aeroplane*, **88**, 28 Jan. 1955, 106–7.
[30] ZIEBLAND, H., *Jnl. Brit. Int. Soc.*, **14**, 5, Sept.–Oct. 1955, 248–64.
[31] ZIEBLAND, H., *Jnl. Brit. Int. Soc.*, **13**, 3, May 1954, 129–41.
[32] BAXTER, A. D., *Jnl. Brit. Int. Soc.*, **10**, 3, May 1951, 123–38.
[33] SMITH, E. T. B., *Jnl. Brit. Int. Soc.*, **12**, 2, March 1953, 53–62.
[34] TSIEN, H. S., *Jnl. Amer. Rocket Soc.*, **22**, 5, Sept.–Oct. 1952, 256–62, 268.
[35] MARBLE, F., COX, D. W., *Jnl. Amer. Rocket Soc.*, **23**, 2, March 1953.

CHAPTER III

GUIDANCE AND CONTROL

◎

ALTHOUGH the push-botton warfare envisaged as arising from the successful guided weapons system may at first appear to be the latest idea of combat, basically this is not so. Warfare developed from personal combat between adversaries. Bare fists were replaced by primitive weapons which could be held in the hand. The essential of early warfare was that a lethal blow was always under the control of the person making it. At a later stage spears made it possible for blows to be delivered at a distance, but never so accurately as in hand-to-hand fighting. The invention of levers and of means of storing energy so that it could be released rapidly, for example in bows and in gunpowder, gave impetus to the production of improved versions of the simple spear. Missiles came into their own as a main war weapon. But all such missiles were controlled only in so far as they were held in the arm of the warrior or in the throwing mechanism. They were aimed, but when in flight to their target they were at the mercy of the elements and any asymmetry of poor construction. Nevertheless they ultimately gave rise to field artillery and bombers.

The idea of the guided missile, however, goes right back to the beginning; a reversion to personal combat. The death-dealing blow is delivered by a weapon which is at all times controlled by a brain able to guide it and to allow for any feints or evasions of the adversary.

But instead of the skill of the muscles and the quick reactions of the primitive fighting man we now have the scientific ingenuity of his descendants creating swift-reacting electromechanical 'brains' which can control the guided weapons of to-day. Combat again takes on the primitive personal note, but it is machine against machine in place of man against man.

For any guided weapon system the accent must be upon guidance.

This has been the chief problem to cause delay in bringing the new weapons into service.[1]

Guidance covers two distinct technical problems; first the control of the attitude of the missile, and secondly, the control of the path of the missile. The former ensures correct orientation of the vehicle in space, while the latter has to be solved so that the missile will reach its target. Moreover, attitude control must be effected before path guidance can be attempted.

There are essentially three stages in the guidance of any missile. First is known as the *launching phase* when control must be employed in order to correct any dispersion following the take-off, so that the missile can be directed into the correct path for it to enter the next phase of *mid-course guidance*. Then the guidance system must ensure that the missile's warhead is carried as close as possible to the target with the minimum of time delay. The missile next enters its final stage of *terminal guidance* in which it has to be brought within lethal distance of the target. Finally the warhead must be exploded; or, if lethal distance is not achieved, a safety device has to operate so that the missile cannot damage friendly personnel or equipment.

Missile guidance systems can be conveniently divided into two classes each of which has its own special peculiarities. The first covers all missiles which move against surface targets—such as the broad categories of surface-to-surface and air-to-surface missiles— where the target is essentially stationary and its position on the surface of the Earth can be observed or calculated. The second class encompasses those missiles which are designed to attack moving targets, mainly surface-to-air missiles and air-to-air missiles. These two broad categories cover most missiles but there are, of course, borderline cases; for example, air-to-sea and underwater-to-air missiles, which do not fit quite so readily into the general pattern.

The three stages of guidance operate somewhat differently in each class. For weapons which are directed against airborne targets, the first stage following launching often consists of a radar gathering beam having a wide conical form which can bring the missile to the correct flight path as already mentioned. During mid-course guidance the missile can use what is known as beam rider or a system of command guidance, while the final closing to the kill will make use of some kind of homing device.

For surface-to-surface missiles, the launching phase will once more be used to place the missile on its correct initial flight path or trajectory. Mid-course guidance in this class has to extend over a much longer range and will make use of an inertial or navigational system, while target homing might include a device to explode the thermonuclear warhead at the optimum distance from the target area, which may not be at closest approach to the target.

The beam rider system of control (*Fig. 3.1a*) is mainly used for ground-to-air missiles. It depends upon a narrow coded radio beam which is locked on to the target by radar. The missile is gathered by a wide-angle beam during the initial phase and brought into the tight control beam. The internal guidance system of the missile then keeps it centred on the tight beam leading to the target. The width of the control beam is important, for if it is too wide the missile will miss the target at long ranges, while a beam which is too tight

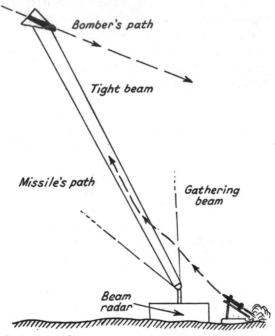

Two types of missile guidance.

FIG. 3.1(*a*) *Beam rider uses one radar tracker while the missile has sensing elements which enable it to fly up the beam to the target. A gathering beam is used to collect the missile after launching and to bring it into the tight controlling beam.*

60

may lose the missile during the final manœuvres where rapid transverse accelerations are needed. Another problem associated with beam rider is that the beam can be reflected from various parts of large bombers and give rise to inaccuracies because the beam is not centred exactly on the target.

Command guidance, also used for ground-to-air weapons, is a simple system as far as the missile is concerned because the control of its flight path comes from the ground station rather than from sensing devices in the missile itself as in beam rider. Essentially the command guidance system uses two radars, one for tracking the target while the other tracks the missile. In early systems a human controller had to align blips on a cathode-ray tube but now completely automatic devices are employed. The outputs from the two tracking radars are fed into a computer on the ground (*Fig. 3.1b*)

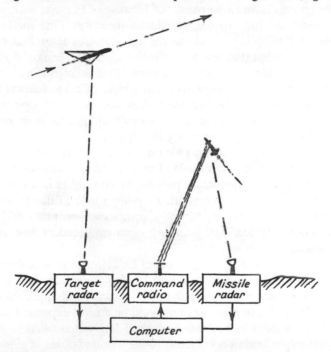

FIG. 3.1(*b*) *The Command Guidance system uses two radar trackers, one to follow the target while the other follows the missile. A computer uses the data from the two tracking radars to issue instructions to the missile through a command link.*

which determines the commands which have to be transmitted to the missile for it to intercept the target aircraft. These instructions are sent by radio from the fourth component in the system, the command radio. The only equipment carried in the missile is a radio receiver, a decoder for the command signals, and servomechanisms needed to operate the missile control surfaces.

Although the dropping of 'window' could confuse the early systems of both beam rider and command guidance, this is not so to-day where advanced radar installations can quickly differentiate between the fast-moving target and the cloud of tin-foil strips which, because of their great drag, rapidly lose any forward velocity which they possess when released from the invading aircraft.

But both systems are susceptible to other enemy counter-measures, and to jamming, resistance to which becomes essential. Many simple systems have to be ruled out because of the ease with which they would fall prey to enemy counter-measures. One method of avoiding jamming is to send the control impulses at various coded frequencies so that they are only effective when the series of different frequencies arrives in a certain pattern. This is known as a radio lock because it is analogous to the tumblers of a mechanical lock. But as anti-jamming devices form such an important part of the design of guidance systems all modern developments must remain highly classified from the security standpoint.

Beam rider and command guidance have the advantage of minimum equipment in the missile. For expendable defence missiles this is an important factor. By putting the computers and expensive radar equipment on the ground, they are made available for the guidance of many missiles. Airborne equipment becomes merely the beam sensing device, anti-jamming circuits, decoders and servo-mechanisms.

On the other hand the missile might be designed to be completely independent of ground control and to contain within itself all the equipment needed for it to track down its target and approach close enough for a kill. In practice this would be a most expensive way of controlling a defensive missile and accordingly it is usual to apply internal missile 'brainwork' merely to the terminal phase of guidance, when it is known as a homing technique.

Most missiles nowadays incorporate some system of homing to close in on their targets without control from the ground station.

Homing can be passive where the missile is attracted by a source of energy in the target, for example heat, electromagnetic waves or noise, radiated from the aircraft's engines or equipment, or even heat radiation arising from the aerodynamic heating of fast-moving bodies. The equipment in the missile then consists of sensitive directional detectors which can operate the servo controls to put the missile on the correct heading for it to achieve interception.

A semi-active homing system uses radiation from the target which is produced by the defences. Analogous to the old anti-aircraft searchlights a powerful radar transmitter called 'lamp-set' is used to illuminate the target. The detectors in the missile then home on the radiation reflected from the target aircraft or missile. Sometimes the 'lamp-set' is carried in a mother aircraft for use with air-to-air missiles.

The most advanced stage is however known as active homing, in which the missile contains the means of emitting its own searching radar impulses.

All homing systems have fairly short ranges. Passive homing on infra-red radiation may have a maximum range—at night—of only about ten miles. The declassified systems have many shortcomings but the most modern developments have to remain restricted. The fact that missiles are being put into production[2] implies that more reliable systems have now been developed. (*Fig.* 3.2.)

Self-destruction units are required in missile work. An example is a small compact unit produced by Graseby Instruments Ltd., which consists of a clockwork mechanism designed to effect the break-up of a missile after a pre-determined time interval. The mechanism is started by means of an inertia switch, and the release of the escapement can be adjusted to a wide range of acceleration. In order to prevent the mechanism from operating prematurely, a safety catch is embodied in the design which will prevent operation unless an acceleration force of a pre-set value is maintained for a given period of time.[3]

The optimum choice of guidance system is bound up with the interception course of the missile. The simplest attack is known as 'dog pursuit' in which the missile is heading towards its target at each instant of its flight. (*Fig.* 3.3a.)[4] This approach is not convenient because the final stage of closing to the kill demands excessive accelerations. The trajectory of the missile is a curve which has a

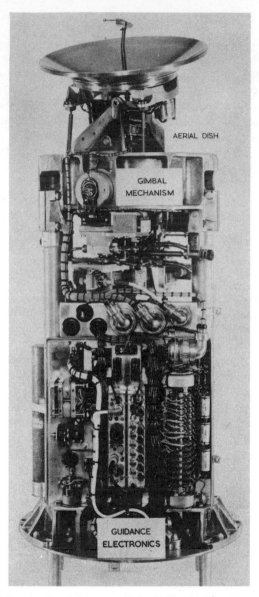

FIG. 3.2. *A homing head for a guided missile showing the aerial dish and the rotating scanner, the gimbal mechanism and the associated electronics. This illustrates the complexity of homing devices which have to be carried even in small anti-aircraft devices.*

(Photo. Elliott Bros. Ltd.)

decreasing radius of curvature as the target is approached. The lateral acceleration of the missile is continually increasing, and at an ever increasing rate. Contact with the target would demand an impossibly high acceleration so the best which can be obtained is a near miss.

The disadvantages can be overcome by arranging for the missile to anticipate where the target is going to be. The system of proportional navigation makes the missile 'think', so that instead of heading always directly towards the target as in the previous case, the controls within the missile ensure that the rate of change of heading is proportional to the rate of change of the line of sight between the

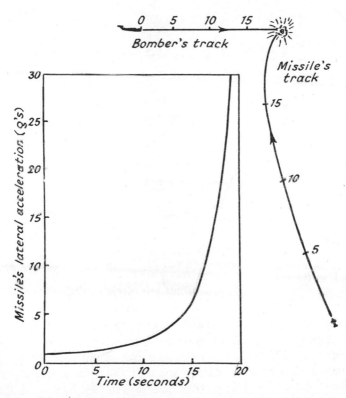

Two elementary systems of interception.
FIG. 3.3(*a*) '*Dog' pursuit in which the missile is always heading towards the* *target.* (Courtesy, Chartered Mechanical Engineer, Ref. 4)

missile and the target. The constant of proportionality is chosen to minimize the lateral acceleration. (*Fig.* 3.3(*b*).)

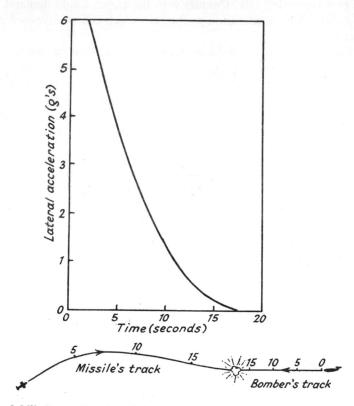

FIG. 3.3(*b*) *Proportional guidance where the missile anticipates the future position of the target.*

(Courtesy, Chartered Mechanical Engineer, Ref. 4)

Surface-to-surface missiles and air-to-surface missiles again use a three-stage guidance. The initial stage in the case of ground-launched missiles is used to place them on the correct flight path for winged missiles, or moving at the correct speed on the ballistic trajectory at all-burnt in the case of long-range ballistic vehicles. In air-to-surface missiles it will consist of navigating the aircraft to the correct position for launching the missile. Plotted trajectory systems, which have definite range limitations, rely upon surface radar to plot the course of the missile so that guidance control impulses can be sent to it or the terminal guidance phase can be initiated. A coded radar responder is used in the missile.

The most critical control problem is that associated with the launching of multi-stage rocket vehicles. Small errors in trajectory and all-burnt velocity of, say, a third stage can place the missile well off its target. As this class of missile represents perhaps the ultimate in guided weapon development all details of such control systems are restricted. Nevertheless it is known that considerable improvements over the V-2 guidance system have been made.[5]

Because long-range missiles are invariably expensive items of equipment, and are necessarily expendable, it is sound economy to include within them even more expensive control equipment so that they may be assured of reaching their target.

The one declassified system which is completely free of outside interference is the pre-set inertial guidance system. In effect a complete electronic memory and navigational system is built into the missile. By a suitable frame of reference, such as a natural one like a sunseeker/magnetometer device or a star-tracker, or an artificial one like a Loran network, the missile fixes its own position in space and follows a pre-determined course to the target the co-ordinates of which have been fixed in its 'memory'. The essential of any long-range guidance system is that it should be free from jamming and also accurate and incapable of giving warning to the enemy. The inertial guidance seems best to suit these requirements and some instrumentations have already been tested in aircraft flights over long ranges where their accuracy has been proved.[6] In fact, dead reckoning aircraft navigational systems are commercially available which are accurate to within 5 miles in 1,000 miles, and with ranges of up to 3,000 miles.

The basis of the inertial guidance system is a supersensitive accelerometer which can accurately detect longitudinal and transverse accelerations. Coupled with three of these accelerometers are accurate gyroscopes which have very little precession* and which can accordingly act as a frame of reference for the missile.

A typical missile directional gyroscope is shown in (*Fig.* 3.4). This is manufactured by Gyromechanisms, of New York, and weighing

---

*Precession is the term applied to the conical motion of the axis of momentum of a rotating body caused by the action of an external couple.

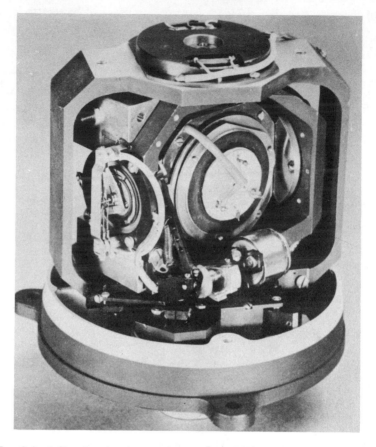

FIG. 3.4. *A directional gyroscope for use in missiles which weighs only 5·5 lb and is capable of withstanding an acceleration of thirty times that of gravity.*
(Photo. Gyromechanisms Inc.)

$5\frac{1}{2}$ lb (2·5 kg) has a diameter of only 5 in (12·7 cm). The inner axis has a gimbal freedom of 85 deg, while that of the outer axis is unlimited. Pick-offs are in the form of a mechanical switch and a potentiometer respectively. An induction motor takes a running current of only 0·1 amps, needing less than 6·0 watts of power. The unit is started 1 min before it can reach satisfactory operating speed. A directional gyroscope of this nature can operate in temperature conditions varying from -55 to $+70°$ C and at ambient pressures from zero to two atmospheres. It can withstand a shock of 30 G and severe vibrations, and can be stored unused up to five years.[7] The latter is an important criterion for use in defensive missiles.

One of the latest type of gyroscopes uses air bearings. These reduce friction to almost negligible amounts so that the precession is very nearly absent. These gyroscopes are for use in intercontinental guidance systems.

Before the long-range missile is launched, all the forces which are likely to affect it are computed and are recorded in its internal memory by means of a small storage device forming part of the internal electronic computer. Then, during flight, if the accelerometers send data to the computer which are at variance with those stored in its memory, corrections are made immediately and automatically. There is a large number of unpredictable forces which can thus act on the missile. These include wind gusts, variation in the physical conditions of the upper atmosphere, for example, temperature and density, unpredicted variations in power plant performance, and malfunctioning of the control surfaces. The deflection from the pre-calculated path is sensed and error signals are then fed from the computer through the servomechanisms to give the required change of control surfaces, motor angle, or power plant thrust for the missile to return to its pre-set flight path or trajectory.

Such systems can be improved upon if a certain amount of reference co-ordinate checking can be done during the flight. This is especially important over long ranges. Checking of co-ordinates can be done automatically by the missile using a star-tracking device which observes certain bright stars, or by using measurements of the Earth's magnetic field or by utilizing some artificial hyperbolic grid system whereby two or more stations transmit overlapping signals to form a radio grid over the route to the target. The receiver in the missile measures the time delay between signals received from the two stations and is able to translate this delay into an accurate positional reference. Examples of such systems are in common use in commercial aviation but they are susceptible to enemy countermeasures and to certain weather conditions.

The star-tracker utilizes two optical devices which are aligned on selected stars, and by using the position of the substellar point (the point on the Earth's surface where an imaginary line from the star to the Earth's centre passes through the surface) the position of the missile can be accurately controlled. This equipment needs a stable platform but nowadays such platforms are available for both winged and ballistic type missiles.[8]

The substellar point is the position on the globe of the Earth where the star is at that instant directly overhead. These positions can be calculated very accurately. Moreover, if at any position of the missile the star can be observed, then that position of the missile can be calculated. The angle between the missile, the centre of the Earth and the substellar point is equal to the zenith distance* of the star as observed from the missile. By using two stars it is possible to find the position of the missile relative to the two substellar points and thus exactly fix its position on the globe of the Earth. The intersection of the two position circles could give rise to ambiguity if the stars were not carefully chosen.

A typical intercontinental missile might incorporate several systems of guidance. During the launching phase there will be beam guidance followed by mid-course inertial guidance with celestial or artificial-reference-frame navigation. Finally, passive homing on infra-red, light waves, or magnetic fields will bring the nuclear warhead to within lethal distance of the target area.

The essential feature of missile guidance is that the equipment within the missile must be capable of withstanding high accelerations, longitudinally during the take-off period and then laterally during manœuvres.

The warhead size and power is also of great importance in determining how close the guidance system must bring the missile to its target. A curve can be drawn showing warhead weight as a function of miss distance for a definite kill. This curve rises very steeply as the miss distance increases (*Fig.* 3.5)[9] and it is the problem of the guidance engineers to ensure that for a given missile and warhead weight the closest appraoch and the warhead weight position should lie in the cross-hatched portion of the figure.

It is found that if the guidance system cannot give a close approach the warhead weight goes up alarmingly. This will mean either a shorter range for the missile or that the take-off weight for a given range will correspondingly increase. With chemical explosive warheads, therefore, the aim of the guidance system engineer must

*Zenith distance is the angle between the star and the zenith.

be to obtain the closest possible approach to the target. If thermo-nuclear warheads become a common payload of missiles as well they might[10] the problem is eased considerably, for they can be exploded at a considerable distance from the target yet still be effective. While this type of warhead will undoubtedly be used in long-range missiles, it is unlikely that, at this stage, all anti-aircraft missiles will so be equipped. As far as anti-missile missiles are concerned it may be essential to have nuclear warheads with large lethal volume in order to be certain of interception.

Component selection for guided missile application is of great importance. Most supersonic missiles are noisy which naturally implies the presence of vibrations. These vibrations can open relays and even destroy equipment so that it becomes necessary for components to be tested prior to missile use by means of a machine which is known as a 'shaker' and which can subject them to a range of frequencies up to at least 500 cycles per second. Acceleration effects can also be troublesome. Again they can upset relays unless these are exactly balanced, and they can result in bearings burning

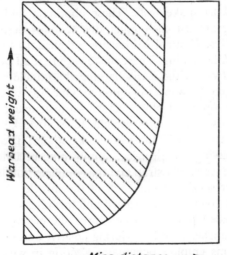

Fig. 3.5. *Curve showing warhead weight plotted against miss distance, showing how the warhead weight rises very rapidly if the guidance engineers cannot make the missile approach close to the target.*

(Courtesy, Chartered Mechanical Engineer, Ref. 4)

out due to the increased loads placed upon them. Early missiles had to utilize makeshift adaptations of existing commercial equipment. Modification was necessary to give compatibility with missile environment, and many failures were encountered. Nowadays more equipment is being designed specifically for use in guided weapons with a result that greater reliability is being achieved.

During test programmes it has been found that many electronic failures occur at launching because of the high shock loads produced by the booster acceleration. It is then too late to postpone the launching and the missile has had to be written off as a complete loss. In addition, missile components suffer extremes of temperature. Basic missile design calls for miniaturization of equipment and this in turn means that power dissipation problems are serious in the confined missile space. At the same time heat comes into the missile from outside due to aerodynamic heating at the high speeds involved. Even with short flying times some kind of refrigeration becomes necessary.

An extensive programme of testing is needed for all missile components; they are subjected to acceleration tests on centrifugal machines and to shake tests. These eliminate faulty connexions, wires shorting against each other due to poor design, and faulty electronic valves. Control cables are attached to the missile until the moment of launching. These make sure that all pre-flight checks can be carried out without discharging the missile batteries. But a method of rapid disconnect is required. One way of doing this is to use a solenoid operated plug ejector. An instrument manufactured by Graseby Instruments Ltd., weighs 16 oz (0·45 kg) and develops an ejection pressure of 32 lb sq in (2·3 kg/sq cm). It operates on the principle of having the electrical supply plug attached securely to the ejector by means of a strap and the complete unit is then inserted into the power socket on the shell of the missile. When launching takes place the solenoid is energized and this releases simultaneously two spring-loaded plungers which force the ejector and plug well clear of the launcher thereby ensuring positive and rapid ejection.

Other systems employ pneumatic ejection in which air pressure operates the plungers which force the plug from the socket in the missile skin. Higher ejection pressures are available with pneumatic than with electrical ejectors.[11]

The guidance of missiles depends entirely on the science of electronics which basically relies upon devices which are able to amplify electrical impulses, changes in current or in voltage or both. For many years the main device used to produce amplification was the thermionic valve. A large proportion of valves obtained commercially were found not to be suitable for use in missiles. It became common practice in many missile companies to test all such valves before they were passed for airborne use in their missiles. They would be shake-tested and then examined optically with a microscope for internal flaws.[12] (*Fig.* 3.6.) Some companies used X-ray examination in

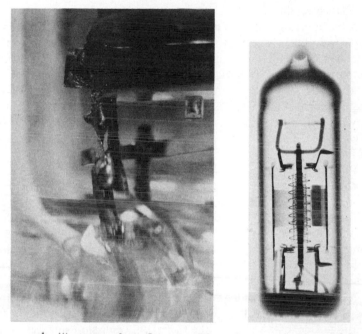

Photographs illustrating how flaws in radio valves can be detected by a pre-flight inspection.

(*a*) *A microscopic examination can show faulty supports which may allow the electrode assembly to collapse during the high accelerations at boosted take-off.*

(*b*) *Shows how the internal structure of the radio valve can be examined critically by suitable X-ray photographs. This type of examination makes it possible to detect flaws hidden by the other electrodes.*

(Photos. North American Aviation Inc.)

FIG. 3.6

73

addition, and also a pre-aging of the valves, running them for a specified period of time to ensure that they were functioning correctly.[13] Recently, stacked radio valves have come into production and find use in missiles simply because they can be applied in conventional electronic circuits. Ceramic caps replace the glass bulb, and ceramic spacers between the electrodes give great mechanical strength for small size. One of these modern valves is claimed to be capable of operating while glowing red hot at a temperature of 540° C.

In a number of cases magnetic amplifiers find application in missiles in order to dispense with vacuum tubes.[14] They are superior as far as resistance to shock and vibration is concerned. Moreover they are capable of greater ratios of power amplification to response time than rotary amplifiers, and they require little maintenance. They are particularly useful in the control of servomechanisms. The magnetic amplifier is basically a variable impedance device which controls the load power and voltage. Amplification occurs because the power requirements of the control source is many times less than the control power applied to the load. Nowadays, self-saturating types like the Westinghouse *Megamp* have come into prominent use in many fields of industry.

But the transistor gives the greatest possibilities for miniaturized control systems of missiles because of low power dissipation as heat.[15] Especially will this be so when circuits are redesigned for pure transistor use. At the present moment production of transistors is still low in quantity while costs are high, but development is continuing. For high temperature applications the new silicon transistors hold great promise. At the moment however their cost is about six times as much as that of a thermionic valve.

A transistor is one of a group of devices which use semi-conductors for their operation.[16] It is able to amplify without the need for the heating of delicate parts like the thermionic emission surfaces of the normal valve. Although the transistor is a very new electrical device it is basically developed from the old 'cat's whisker' crystal detector. It functions on a controlled electron flow within a solid semi-conductor. These solids have resistances higher than copper but less than that of insulators like glass. In fact the resistance of the semi-conductor increases with the purity of the specimen. Two types are available, N-type in which the pure semi-conductor uses an impurity which has more electrons in the outer orbits of its atoms than does the semi-conductor. This is known as a negative carrier. Alternatively the P-type or positive carrier uses an impurity having less electrons in the outer orbits than the semi-conductor. The deficiency of electrons results in the phenomenon of 'holes' whereby the equivalent of positively-charged particles can migrate through the mass of the semi-conductor. The flow of electrons and flow of holes results in an amplification.[17]

Most transistors use the element germanium as the semi-conductor. The first transistors were of the point-contact type which can give a current gain greater than unity but is prone to generating plenty of noise. This type of transistor has, nevertheless, high frequency capabilities even up to 300 Mc/s and it therefore finds use in radio frequency oscillators and amplifiers, in intermediate frequency amplifiers and in switching circuits. It is not suitable for amplification where the noise level would limit the smallest size of signal capable of being amplified. One particular useful application is in the flip-flop circuit employed in digital computers. The transistor gives a great saving in power and space requirements and only one transistor is required in place of two radio valves for this circuit.

The other type of transistor is the junction transistor and this shows considerable improvement in noise level. It can accordingly be used to amplify faint signals. It gives appreciable power gain without change in current because the emitter has high impedance while that of the collector is quite low. This is desirable for stability in the electronic circuits but the capacity effect of the wafer construction used in this type of transistor limits the frequency at which it can be used to less than 200 kc/s. It is accordingly used as an amplifier and oscillator at low frequencies only. Experimental n-p-n junction tetrode transistors have however operated at 1,000 Mc/s.

Generally it is found that transistors consume about 1,000th of the power of a radio valve. They are small and have no warming-up period so that they are ready for instant use. Transistors are used directly from, say, 12 volts, and thus they eliminate high voltage generators such as vibrator units which are notorious sources of trouble.

A transistorized power conversion unit which replaces dynamotors, vibrator packs, or high tension batteries[18] weighs 1·6 lb (0·73 kg) compared with 4·75 lb (2·15 kg) of a standard rotary converter with a similar output. It takes up half the cubic volume, gives closer voltage regulation, has no vibration, an almost instantaneous start without a starting surge and has excellent resistance to acceleration. Moreover, the high frequency of its operation reduces the weight of the smoothing circuits. An excessive load simply stops operation so that a load short-circuit does not damage the power pack. Although the voltage output is stable over a considerable temperature range, power output falls at elevated temperatures. Germanium transistors permit operation up to 70° C, while silicon is now finding increasing application in transistor manufacture because of its ability to operate at higher temperatures.

Scientists of Bell Telephone Laboratories have developed a new type of silicon power rectifier which may have unlimited life span and can operate at temperatures up to 200° C.[19] Treatment with vapours at high temperature causes a minute trace of impurities to enter the crystalline structure of the silicon to form a p-n junction. Two of the new rectifiers when made about the size of peas linked together and mounted on a cooling fin furnished more than 20 amperes of direct current at 100 volts. This amounts to 2,000 watts with only 20 watts lost through heat. Each of the rectifiers contained a silicon wafer 0·005 in (0·015 cm) in thickness and 0·1 in (0·25 cm) square. They provided 5,000 times more current than conventional rectifiers of the same size, and could thus be used for the miniature operating units which are required in missiles.

One problem with transistors has been that of turning out mass produced transistors having constant and predictable characteristics. One American company has claimed however that a new method of producing v.h.f. transistors has been developed which permits a much greater improvement over the normal transistor rejection rate of some 40 to 50 per cent.[20]

In addition to the means of amplification, electronic devices need wiring, and in the past the conventional method of wiring by individually soldered joints has led to innumerable failures, to high-resistance joints, and to open circuits. To avoid these faults all branches of the radio and electronic industry are trying printed circuits. Particularly is this so in the missile industry.

The most widely used method of producing printed circuits is to print the shape of the required connexions on the copper surface of a sheet of laminated plastic and later to remove the unwanted areas of unprinted copper by an etching process.[21] For this purpose

Bakelite Ltd. produce a copper-clad laminate which consists of a phenolic-laminated base to which the copper foil is bonded. The surface resistivity of the base material is very high, exceeding 5×10^4 Megohms/cm^2. A layer of anti-tracking backing material is exposed on the surface of the base material by the etching process as it has been found[22] that unless anti-tracking backing is used fingerprints, put on the base material during handling, can give shorts when completed circuits are later exposed to humid conditions, due to the fingerprints being hygroscopic.

Printed circuits show a reduction in cost because small components such as low-capacity coupling condensers and tuning inductors may be printed in the circuit at no extra cost. (*Fig.* 3.7.) This technique of

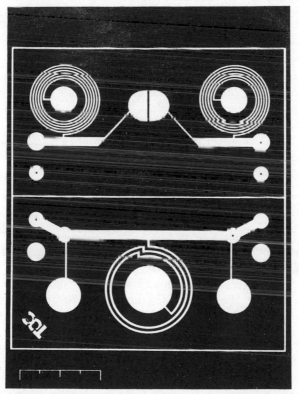

FIG. 3.7. *Example of how radio-frequency coils and condensers can be included in a printed circuit.* (Photo. Telegraph Condenser Co.)

printing circuits is especially suitable for transistor amplifiers, and for filter networks employing coils and condensers, for frame aerials, computer panels, and for constancy and reproducibility of inductances in tuned filter circuits. Printed circuits also give reduced hum level in high-gain amplifiers and have the tremendous advantage over conventional circuits as far as mass production is concerned in that identical wiring is guaranteed. For missiles this is important as is also the great dimensional advantage of producing thin, flat, circuits which can make best use of available space. To improve space factors still further, three-dimensional wiring can be made by the use of a flexible folding base. An example is the production of radio-frequency transformers. Also intermediate frequencies between 35 and 38 Mc/s can use a printed circuit amplifier with printed coils and condensers. High pass filters for eliminating interference in the aerial circuit[23] and anti-jamming circuits can be printed in this way. Servo amplifiers with printed resistors have also been successfully manufactured.[24]

A further great advantage of the printed circuit lies in the fact that components can be laid out in such a way that all points of interconnexion lie in the same plane. They can be connected together simultaneously by the technique of dip soldering, thus obviating the considerable time spent in manually soldering connexions. Similarly many tags, eyelets and screws are eliminated. The printed circuit ensures that all components are accurately positioned so that capacitative and inductive effects can be accurately calculated and duplicated from set to set. As the laminated base is also used as a chassis, insulated bases are minimized, and sleeving and insulated resistors eliminated. This again saves weight.

The dip-soldering technique now used[25] is to position the components on the reverse side of the printed circuit chassis. The wire ends are cut to size leaving a small kink so that when they are sprung into the holes in the chassis the components do not fall out again. The printed circuit side is then sprayed with flux after which it is floated on top of a bath of solder. The molten metal adheres to the copper circuit and to the ends of the wires of the components. Vibration is employed to remove oxide, and the circuit is dipped for a second time. This method produces uniform connexions and is very easily adapted for assembly-line production. Sometimes the copper surface is also coated with silver to increase conductivity, but the printed circuit basically has wiring which has a large surface area compared with its cross-sectional area, so that the connexions can readily dissipate heat and thus carry heavier currents than conventional wires of the same cross-sectional area.

Electronic equipment needs power for its operation and this was developed by wind-driven generators in the earliest German missiles.[26] Nowadays it is obtained from electrical batteries within the missile and from solid-propellant power packs. The most suitable type of battery for this purpose appears to be the silver cell which is assembled as a light-weight accumulator. The positive plates are of pure silver and these are separated from the negative plates of zinc oxide by a cellulosic material which allows good diffusion of the electrolyte, while at the same time preventing a migration of metallic particles from one plate to the other.[27]

No grids or other forms of support are necessary because the excellent conductivity of the materials used removes any necessity of grid current distribution. The electrolyte is the strong alkali KOH which is held mainly absorbed in the cellulosic material general assembly. As the whole accumulator is confined under lateral pressure within the case it can resist shocks arising from acceleration and vibration. Gassing is almost completely absent because the electrolyte does not take any part in the reaction of the accumulator. A further advantage of the cell for missile application is that it will retain its charge up to a period of one year under conditions of normal temperature, and that it gives a very high rate of discharge between operating temperatures of $-50°$ C and $+60°$ C. Moreover, the cell shows no tendency to boil at the reduced pressures encountered at high altitudes. Silver cell batteries have indeed proved reliable at heights of up to 85 miles (136 km).[28] The normal voltage of a single cell is 1·5 volts, and an 80 ampere-hour accumulator can be made to weigh only 28 oz (0·8 kg). One small experimental cell weighing 0·75 oz (0·021 kg) gave 40 amperes when short circuited.[29] In missile work where space and weight are at a premium, the silver cell becomes an important piece of equipment.

The other type of power supply for missiles relies upon the consumption of a solid-propellant.[30] A unit of this nature is shown in *Fig.* 3.8. It gives 130 atmospheres regulated hydraulic pressure within 2 sec after ignition, and this is maintained for 25 sec, during which period a constant speed alternator produces 1,750 VA. The entire power package occupies a segment of a cylinder with a 5·5 in (12·7 cm) radius and included angle of 195 deg. Its overall length is 14·25 in (36·2 cm) and its total weight is 36 lb (16·3 kg). Hydraulic flow is 2 gal per min (9 litres/min) and the unit will operate at ambient pressures ranging from sea level to 50,000 ft (15,000 m) and under acceleration loads up to 38 G longitudinally and 15 G along any other direction.

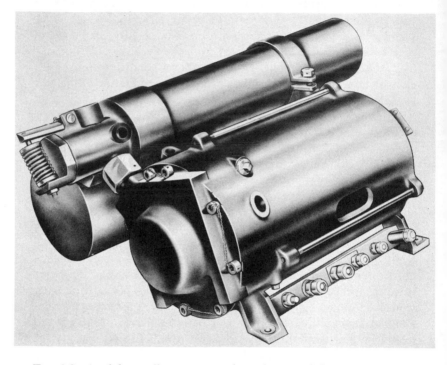

Fig. 3.8. *A solid propellant power package for a guided missile. Weighing only 36 lb it supplies both electrical and hydraulic power for a period of 25 sec.*

(Photo. Hamilton Standard)

Having received the controlling signal and decoded it, the next stage is for the guidance system to operate servomechanisms which will give the necessary course correction by using aerodynamic forces or thrust forces derived from the power plant itself.

When a missile design gives rise to a vehicle which is very stable in flight this vehicle will need large control forces to execute manœuvres. On the other hand if the missile is unstable, the control forces required may be small in magnitude but must be capable of swift application.

The chief essential in the latter case is that the control should be quick acting and that there should be no oscillation. This latter is avoided by the use of synchros[31] which are single-phase alternating current machines. They usually consist of a two-pole single-phase rotor field and a Y-wound single-phase variable voltage motor. Where it is necessary to amplify the control signal a servomechanism is essential, at the heart of which is a synchro system and which must have a feed back device to produce amplification. Over the past few years more and more use has been made of servomechanisms in industrial applications. These consist of two types, the open loop and the closed loop controlling systems. In the open loop system events are controlled arbitrarily and what is being controlled can have no effect upon the controlling device. Essentially in the open loop system there is nothing in the mechanism to measure the result of the application, and consequently nothing is done to rectify any errors made by the controlling system. Most application is, however, found for what are known as closed loop control systems, where the results of the operation are fed back into the control circuits so that they can rectify errors. The main feature of the closed loop control system is that something is done about errors and the ideal to be aimed at is that the errors should remain zero at all times. In various types of control systems it was man himself who closed the loop; his judgement of the results of the control process enabled him to effect the control needed to give the minimum error. In missiles, of course, man does in some instances assist in closing the loop, but as far as the missile itself is concerned the usual method is to have the control effected by means of an electromagnetic system which senses errors, and feeds back the necessary corrections to minimize these errors. The servo-loop is then closed by controlling impulses coming from the ground control and also by error-sensing devices within the missile.

The basic operation of the servomechanism is therefore to amplify the control signal, pass this to the control surfaces to actuate them and to take account of any error signals picked up by sensing devices within the missile. Operation of the control surfaces is accomplished by means of servomotors which may be electrical, pneumatic or hydraulic in their operation. Servo actuators should need low standby power and should be small in size but quick in operation. Many missiles use a tail-first configuration in which cruciform control surfaces rotate as a whole. The NIKE, for example, uses this method of control. Other missiles which may have still to be controlled in regions of the upper atmosphere where aerodynamic forces are almost absent, may rely upon a swivelling motor mounted on gimbals. Pilotless aircraft types of configurations use the conventional aircraft systems.

For winged long-range missiles powered by ramjets and turbojets it is necessary to control speed and altitude during the flight to the target. Indeed a programme might be chosen so that these are continuously varied in a pre-determined manner in order to confuse the defences. A differential pressure monitor might be used for this purpose.[32] One pressure is fed to the inside of a diaphragm, the other to the inside of the sealed instrument where it acts as the outside pressure of the diaphragm. As the pressure varies, the diaphragm moves a rocking shaft and its motion can be adjusted by a calibrating arm. Attached to the rocking shaft is a c-shaped iron armature, while a field structure carries four symmetrically-wound coils which act as an inductive bridge system. When the armature is centred in the field structure the bridge is balanced and the monitor output is zero. When the armature is moved there is an output voltage from the bridge which is proportional to the distance of the armature from the central position. Changes in ambient temperature are compensated by a bi-metallic compensator element and an electrical network.

Another great problem of missile control is the separation of boosters or of the stages of a multi-step rocket. This separation must take place smoothly and without the generation of any side thrusts. If the release mechanism operates too soon some of the booster power is lost because the boosters can be released while they are still thrusting so that the missile does not achieve its anticipated range. Alternatively, if they are not released at the moment of propellant exhaustion they become unnecessary dead weight and again result in reduced range. Wrap-around boosters are shaped so that aerodynamic forces acting on them will produce separation clear of the missile when release takes place. Tandem boosters fall behind with the continued acceleration of the main missile produced by its sustaining power plant. Difference in thrusts of wrap-around boosters can lead to a moment of force around the centre of gravity of the missile. One method of avoiding this is to incline the nozzles and have their angle of inclination adjustable so as to ensure that the thrust from each booster rocket passes through the centre of gravity of the missile as a whole. Another method is to connect the individual booster rockets by a thrust equalizing manifold.[33]

Boost separation is triggered by an inertia switch. One type[34] is designed to complete an electrical circuit at a pre-determined time after the boost acceleration falls below a certain value. This is accomplished in two distinct phases. First a piston and plunger move back against springs during the initial boost period, the piston then locking and making the first contact to arm the switch. Then secondly, when the acceleration falls at the end of the boost period the plunger is forced forward by its spring and makes contact with the other end of the switch at a set time, so completing the electrical circuit. A silicone damping fluid is used, the viscosity of which can be chosen as desired. By an adjustment in the size of the bleed hole in the piston for arming and the plunger for firing, the time of both of these operations can be adjusted. The strength of the firing spring determines the value of the acceleration at which the plunger will commence to move forward for firing. As an added safety factor, the switch can only operate when an acceleration force of a pre-set value is maintained for a given time period. This switch weighs only 5 oz (0·14 kg) and typical operating conditions might be to arm at 20 G and to fire at 5 G. The switch can be less than 1 in (2·54 cm) in diameter and about 3 in (7·5 cm) in length.

In addition to radio commands going out to the missile it is necessary in the present state of the art for data to be returned to base. Missiles are difficult to produce because they are essentially one-short affairs and usually end up as a tangled heap of wreckage in the desert or on the bottom of the sea. Yet if they are to be perfected engineers have to know exactly what has been happening within them during the flight. Many parameters are accordingly measured, such as propellant consumption rate, voltages in the electrical system, pressures in the hydraulic system, temperatures of the propulsion unit and in the instrumentation and the controls. Also roll, pitch, yaw and wing stresses need to be recorded throughout the flight. (*Fig.* 3.9.) A typical aspect indicator will be mounted at the nose tip and will consist of a swivelling head fitted with two miniature potentiometers. The movement of the head would provide

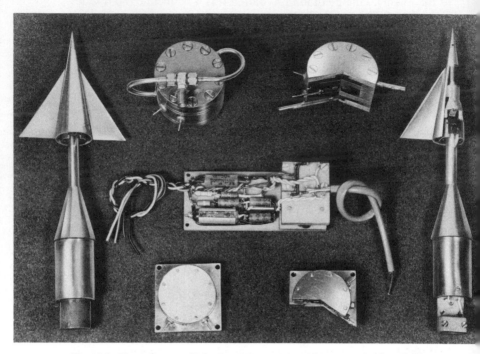

FIG. 3.9. *Transducers which are resistant to acceleration, shock and vibration and have small temperature errors. On the right of the photograph each component is shown in section.*

At the sides are shown an incidence vane system on which the cone and fins are mass balanced about a pivot which is situated well ahead of the centre of pressure. The cone contains a coil and magnetic circuit whose inductance changes 4 m/Henries for an angular change of plus or minus 5 deg of the cone. This instrument determines the aspect of the missile with respect to the airstream.

At the top of the photograph is a pressure transducer consisting of two chambers. A total pressure of 2,500 p.s.i. produces an inductance change of 4 m/Henries. The low range pressure transducer is shown at the bottom and in it a change of only 15 p.s.i. gives the same inductance change as in the high range pressure transducer.

In the centre of the photograph is a magnetic amplifier voltage transducer using a valve oscillator to provide a polarizing alternating current.

(Photo. Bristol Aeroplane Co.)

a linear variation of resistance ratio compared with the angle of yaw. Small compact instruments have a range of ± 12 deg.

Pressure transducers consist of variable inductances or capacities attached to the propellant tanks and propellant lines. By telemetry, which is basically a coded radio broadcast from the missile, these data are sent to the ground station, where they can be studied together with the flight-path data obtained by radar and by optical tracking.

The radio link between the missile and its base has been described as 'an infinitely flexible and elastic cable'. The airborne equipment should be small in the physical size, have low power demands, and yet be capable of simultaneously measuring many different data and types of data. It must moreover be fool-proof and be capable of easy servicing and reliable operation under service conditions. The radio transmission must require only small aerial systems and still have a good range for minimum power requirements. The ground-based equipment also has to be most reliable and easy to operate. It should, moreover, reproduce the data in a form which will facilitate both easy interpretation and permanent recording.

It is convenient to divide a telemetering system into four definite sections. To begin with there is a transducing device which gathers the data to be measured and converts it to a form which is suitable for transmission on a radio-frequency carrier. An encoding device is next used to prepare this transduced data for transmission. The encoding may take the form of amplitude or frequency modulation. The next stage is for the transmitter to radiate the encoded signals to the ground station where the fourth phase commences with the ground station equipment converting the radio signals into facsimiles of the original data signals.

It is usual for the transmissions to be either frequency modulated, phase modulated, or amplitude modulated. One system of time division uses a sequential sampling technique in which a high-speed mechanical switch selects the data to be transmitted at each instant. The physical quantities to be measured are transformed by a trans-ducing device into voltages and the varying amplitudes of these voltages are converted to signals of varying times but of constant amplitude which are then applied to a frequency modulated radio link. In a system of this nature thirty channels can be incorporated in a transmitter which will have a volume of less than 0·1 cu ft (·0028 m³).[33]

Potentiometers when used as transducers must have very low starting torques and must be capable of functioning over a wide range of ambient temperatures. They can however be made extremely small in physical size. One example is less than 1 in (2·54 cm) in diameter by 1 in in length and weighs only 1 oz (0·028 kg). It can give either linear or non-linear output functions and has a resistance value from 200 to 50,000 ohms. The starting torque is only 0·05 in-oz. It can withstand vibration of 10 G to 500 c/s and shock to 60 G.[35]

An alternative system is known as sub-carrier modulation in which the intelligence varies the frequency rather than the amplitude. This can be done by transducers which rely upon a changing capacity or inductance with the parameter to be measured. The sub-carriers are then applied to a frequency-modulated carrier and the system is termed a frequency division system.

An example of a pulse transmitter developed for rocket research is the fifteen channel AN/DKT-7 telemetry transmitter used by the Naval Research Laboratory in the Aerobee rockets to maximum accelerations of 15 G. With a silver cell power supply the whole unit weighed only 32 lb (14.5 kg), the transmitter, having dimensions of 9 × 9 × 12 in (23 × 23 × 30 cm), weighed 18 lb (8·2 kg) and used calibration equipment which had a weight of a further 3½ lb (1·6 kg). Each of the fifteen channels had a normal sampling rate of 312·5 c/s giving an overall rate of 4,700 samples per/sec, at a peak power output of 10 watts.[36]

At the long-range missile test facility of Patrick Air Force Base, Florida, the assigned frequency range for missile telemetry is 216 to 235 Mc/s. It was desired that the receiving aerials should have a 30db gain and low noise. By using an improved helical aerial (giving 20db gain) and a pre-amplifier (20db gain) these conditions were met. The helix consisted of seven turns of 0·25 in (0·63 cm) copper tubing and was 3 ft 9 in (1·14 m) long and 15·25 in (38·7 cm) diameter, giving a beam width varying from 42 to 56 deg. A special multi-coupling device permitted four telemetry receivers to use the same aerial system without mutual interference. Mounted on a 50 ft (15 m) tower this telemetry receiving aerial was able to track missiles for over 1,000 miles (1,600 km) across the sea.[37]

Transistors are now finding use in telemetry circuits as well as in guidance equipment, especially in the airborne sets where they give great saving in space and in power requirements. Various transducers produce a change in resistance, inductance, or capacity with a variation of the parameter being measured. For these various types of transducer different transistor circuits are needed in order to produce oscillation for FM/FM telemetering systems.[38]

Reactance transducers use most advantageously a Hartley oscillator with the tuned circuit between collector and base of the transistor. In the case of resistance circuits the resistance can be used in either of two ways, that is to control the reactance across an L-C tuned circuit by a series or a shunt resistance, or else to use the resistance in a circuit similar to that of a thermionic valve multivibrator. There are requirements that the transistor shall be maintained at constant temperature in order that its characteristics should not vary, but the circuits can be made highly resistant to both shock and vibration.

One of the most important tasks in Britain's guided weapons programme has, indeed, been the development of efficient telemetry equipment, because much information on the behaviour of missiles in flight can only be obtained by equipment which can return the data by radio from the test vehicles. In addition to a high standard of efficiency and reliability, the airborne telemetry transmitters must have high power output, good frequency stability against shock and vibration and decay in power supplies, low cost and weight and small volume.

Telemetry systems can be divided roughly into two main classes. For the measurement of aerodynamic properties such as the position of control surfaces, strains, pressures and torques, a time multiplex or sharing system adequately provides a large number of separate low-frequency response channels. But for measuring the wave forms which occur in airborne electronic equipment, however, channels with a high frequency are required, and the P.P.M. (pulse position modulation) and the time division systems are used.

Two systems, evolved by British Ministry of Supply scientists,[39] fulfil these requirements, each consisting of one type of ground receiver with several varieties of airborne transmitter. They provide adequate and largely complementary coverage for frequency response up to 200–230 cycles. The first gives twenty-three channels for the transmission of data, a further channel being reserved for synchronization, while the second has up to twenty higher frequency channels, any of which can be sub-commutated to give lower frequency channels.

The great advantage of the time multiplex system is that it provides a channel which enables the accuracy of the equipment to be checked throughout its life. At the heart of the airborne section is a rotating sampling switch, the contacts of which connect to transducers which are sampled in turn and each sends its particular message for a small percentage only of the total time. The system accordingly has a low frequency response.

Through the switch the output from the transducers passes to a modulator which generates a sub-carrier at a frequency governed by the voltage or inductance connected to it by the switch wiper. The resultant time multiplexed frequency modulation is used to amplitude modulate a radio frequency oscillator.

At the ground station the data are recorded in two forms; a main low speed record on which any channel or desired combination is displayed separately, and a high speed or histogram record from which all the possible information transmitted by the airborne set can be ascertained by analysis.

Because the transmitter must be fitted to missiles of varying sizes from 3 in (7·6 cm) diameter upwards, flexibility becomes an important design factor. The components of the airborne set have therefore been designed as standard units which can be arranged in various sizes of chassis.

Both the voltage and the inductance types of transducers which are used in the systems are manufactured in a variety of types and ranges. Inductance pick-ups include linear and angular accelerometers, pressure transducers and linear and angular movement pick-ups. Voltage transducers usually take the form of a resistance potentiometer device.

The switch itself consists of a miniature motor, working from a 6·3 volts D.C., driving a four-finger nickel-silver brush assembly in a two-way commutator, moulded in 'Araldite'. On the speed of the switch unit depends the channel frequency response of the system, and three models are available giving speeds of 120, 80 and 40 cycles per sec.

Three types of modulator are in use with the system, one accepting inductance inputs only, one voltage inputs only, and one responding to both types of input. They are built on both sides of a bakelite board and are compact and easy to service. In the case of the inductance responsive modulator, a normal triode oscillator is used, the transducer providing the variable inductance in the tuned circuit. The output of the oscillator is then amplified to give the power needed to modulate the r.f. oscillator. In the second type of modulator the frequency of oscillation of a tuned-grid triode oscillator is controlled by a conventional reactance valve which forms part of its tuned circuit.

In order to provide a combined circuit responding to both voltage and inductance inputs, these two circuits are combined in a four-valve version. The first valve acts as an oscillator for inductance inputs, the second as an amplifier which locks the frequency of the third valve to that of the first. The fourth valve is an amplifier. Voltage inputs render the first valve passive by the damping of its tuned circuit and the voltage is applied as input to the second valve, which, acting as a reactance valve, determines the frequency of oscillation of the third valve. Adequate power for all ranges with minimal D.C. drain is ensured by using two oscillators in the system, having outputs, measured on a C.W. basis, of 1·0 and 8·0 watts respectively. The former oscillator, built in the form of a push-pull tuned-plate/ tuned-grid oscillator uses a specially developed sub-miniature valve. For longer ranges the larger 8 watt unit is used. This has a tuned-anode/tuned grid oscillator built around the CV 397a disc sealed triode. Because the modulator, unaided, cannot control this oscillator, a driver unit is included to supply the necessary power.

Both the oscillators can be arranged to work either C.W. or pulsed, the choice depending largely on compatibility with other r.f. circuits associated with the oscillators in the missile. As these oscillators had to be easily controlled in frequency and had to permit coupling to various aerial systems yet be stable over a wide range of temperatures and pressures, major design problems were involved. Particularly was this so with the 8 watt oscillator, in which high voltages combined with low pressures necessitated considerable development work to prevent flash-over.

For the main ground station record the signal from the missile is demodulated and changed to a series of direct current levels, the step formation thus produced being applied simultaneously to the Y plates of fifteen cathode ray tubes. The synchronizing signal is separated from the output and is used to generate the time base for the large monitor tube and also to produce strobes coinciding with each channel which brighten the traces on the fifteen tubes. The whole fifteen tubes are photographed side by side on a moving film 24 in (61 cm) in width. Also 0·1 sec timing pips and the firing pulse are recorded on each tube while short calibration lines from a crystal frequency generator are added to the record at the completion of each firing.

The high-speed histogram recorder is a self-contained unit for producing records from single channel senders or histogram traces from multichannel transmissions. It contains a receiver and discriminator similar to those in the main equipment but is fed from a separate helical aerial. Data appear as traces on one large and two small cathode ray tubes which are photographed simultaneously by a continuous 35 mm camera. The large tube shows the single channel record or the series of twenty-four direct current levels corresponding to the transmitter channels. One of the small tubes is used to display a time scale, the lateral position of which is calibrated in terms of field strength, and the other small tube indicates any r.f. deviation throughout the missile's flight.

In the P.P.M. system, channel information is given by the time interval between the trailing edge of a reference pulse, which has a total length of about 50 micro-seconds, and the incidence of a 1 micro-second channel pulse. Pulse modulation of the carrier frequency by the reference pulse and the channel pulse takes place, the recurrence frequency of the complete pulse train being between 2,000 and 5,000 per sec, according to the number of transmitter channels. Up to twenty channel pulses, each variable over a range of 400 micro-seconds, can be accommodated between successive reference pulses, but the groups of pulses are usually confined to consecutive intervals of 80 micro-seconds, which is the range of time displayed on each of the five cathode ray tubes in the ground equipment.

Each channel produces directly or via a transducer a variation in voltage which controls the time interval between the trailing edge of a reference square wave and the generation of the respective channel pulse.

The airborne transmitter, the main parts of which are a modulator and an oscillator, is cylindrical in shape with a diameter of 4·5 in (11·5 cm) and an overall length of 6·25 in (15·9 cm) for a twelve-channel set. Manufacture and servicing are facilitated by splitting the modulator into sub-units consisting of a square wave generator and a number of four-channel blocks. Sub-units, 'potted' in marco-resin, can be assembled to form modulators for four, eight, twelve, sixteen, or twenty channels.

The modulator generates a wave form consisting of a wide pulse of approximately 40 micro-seconds width, the trailing edge of which is the time reference for the system, followed by narrow pulses of 1 micro-second width. The wide pulse generator uses a screen-coupled phantastron, from the screen grid of which the pulse, negative in direction, is generated and passed to the grid of a feedback amplifier which inverts it and applies it to the grid of a cathode follower driver. By taking the load of the cathode follower to the bias line in the absence of the positive pulse it cuts off the oscillator grid.

To produce the trigger for the narrow pulse generators the screen grid waveform of the phantastron is also differentiated and applied to the grid of a cathode follower which cuts off the negative pips resulting in a positive trigger pulse at the cathode. This is then coupled to the suppressors of a number of phantastrons through individual diodes which act as D.C. restorers to the negative line through suppressor resistors. In the absence of the trigger the suppressors are held negative and no anode current flows. The screen grids are at a low potential because the screens take the cathode current. When the trigger occurs the anodes begin conducting and, due to the Miller action of the circuit, start their negative voltage excursion, which is fed to the grids by the anode to grid feedback capacitors, tending to cut off the valve current. When this occurs the screen potentials start to rise and, due to the coupling between screen and suppressor, causes the suppressors to be driven and to be held more positive. This feedback sharpens the screen waveform edge. The valves remain in this condition until, at different times depending on the components and inputs controlling the rate of anode run-down, the Miller action ceases. Then the valve's anode can draw no more current, but as the grid tends to go positive, the screen commences drawing current so that its potential falls, and a sudden change-over of current occurs between anode and screen, due to the suppressor grid coupling. The anode remains in this condition because the suppressor is cut off by the screen waveform and the circuit remains in this condition until the arrival of the next trigger pulse.

The screen waveforms are then differentiated to produce a series of negative pulses corresponding to the various 'bottoming' positions of the valves, and which are normally arranged in sets of four, each pulse having an excursion of 80 micro-seconds for full-scale deflection. The groups are constrained to occupy the time scales of 80–160, 160–240, 240–320, 320–400 and 400–480 micro-seconds which represent the time intervals required for full-scale deflection of the five display tubes of the ground equipment. The pulses are then applied to the grid of the feedback amplifier together with the wide pulse, so that the output at the anode is the wide pulse followed by the narrow pulses. This waveform is used to modulate the oscillator.

This latter normally consists of a 2 watt (C.W.) model but for long ranges an 8-watt oscillator has been produced, thereby meeting all requirements between these two extremes of power.

The number of information channels can be increased by introducing a time division switch on them but with a sacrifice in frequency response. Standard switch wafers at present in use have eleven contacts which can be arranged in a number of different ways, for example, four capacity and four voltage channels or eleven voltage channels with the same voltage excursion. As these channels may be arranged to overlap and up to four may be interlaced, identification is needed and is provided by a switch which runs at low speed connecting each input to a fixed voltage in sequence, so that after identification of one channel all the rest follow in order.

The ground equipment of the P.P.M. system produces a maximum of five displays governed by the number of channels in use. The time scales mentioned above are used as the Y time bases for five separate cathode ray tubes, the channel pulses being used as brightening pulses for these traces. Each tube is photographed by a variable-speed continuous 35 mm camera.

After the signal is received at the ground station it is demodulated and then the train of pulses is fed into a voltage circuit box unit, where they are limited and the reference square wave is separated from the channel pulses. A trigger pulse is then generated from the trailing edge of this latter and at each of the five time base generators two phantastron delay circuits are used to develop the appropriate Y axis time base for each display tube. Meanwhile the channel pulses pass through a pulse forming channel and are used as brightening strobes. A timing trace from the master timing system of the missile range is displayed on a small cathode ray tube by the side of each of the channel recording tubes and is photographed with them on the 35 mm film. A pulse from the firing switch displaces this trace to record the time of firing.

As for missile aerial systems these are often beneath radomes and the radiation pattern should be such as to avoid the ionized gases which tend to brush out from the power plant exhaust in the rarefied upper atmosphere. Beam rider devices can be rendered inaccurate by this ionized gas region between the missile and the ground-based beam transmitter. One type of aerial system for operation at 500 to 10,000 Mc/s uses a slot array etched in the outer face of triple plate transmission lines at the end of a wave guide. It gives an aerial system suitable for mounting flush with the skin of the missile or of its wing system.[40]

For some experiments with test vehicles which can be recovered, for example by parachutes or flotation bags, data can be recorded in the missile by means of magnetic tape.[41] The tape record can be recovered (it can even be jettisoned in expendable missiles) and played back at the ground station. A constant reference frequency is used to control automatically the tape speed in its decoding so that the data are correctly transcribed.

The telemetry of data from missiles has been a vital aspect of guided weapon development programmes as will be further discussed in the next chapter.

REFERENCES

[1] ROMICK, D. C., LANIER, H. F., *Aero Digest*, **69**, 1, July 1954, 86, 88, 90, 92, 94.
[2] *Financial Times*, 25 Nov. 1955, p. 1.
[3] GRASEBY INSTRUMENTS LTD., *Data Sheet GW/3/4*, Tolworth, 1955.
[4] GARDNER, G. W. H., *Chart. Mech. Engineer*, **2**, Jan. 1955, 5–22.
[5] SUTTON, G. P., *Jet Propulsion*, **25**, 11, Nov. 1955, 615–26.
[6] ANON., *American Aviation*, **18**, 11, 25 Oct. 1954, 72–74.
[7] GYROMECHANISMS INC., *Data Sheet*, New York, 1955.
[8] STACEY, D. S., *et. al.*, *Electronics*, **27**, Jan. 1954, 149–51.
[9] GARDNER, G. W. H., loc. cit., 4.
[10] ZAEHRINGER, A. J., *Jet Propulsion*, **25**, 9, Part I, Sept. 1955, 473.
[11] GRASEBY INSTRUMENTS LTD., *Data Sheet*, Tolworth, 1955.
[12] KLEINHOFER, B. A., Inst. of Navigation, U.C.L.A., 23 Jan. 1954.
[13] ANON., *American Aviation*, **18**, 11, 25 Oct. 1954, 64–68.
[14] STEIR, H. P., *American Aviation*, **19**, 11, 24 Oct. 1955, 40, 44, 46, 48, 50.

[15] SCHAFFNER, J. S., *General Electric Review*, **57**, 2, Mar. 1954, 50–54.
[16] KRUGMAN, L., *Introduction to Transistors*, Chapman & Hall Ltd., London.
[17] C.B.S. Transistor Manual, *Bulletin E.212.*
[18] TRANSISTOR PRODUCTS INC., *Tech. Data Release*, Waltham, 26 May 1955.
[19] BELL TELEPHONE LABORATORIES, *Press Release*, New York, 7 Jul. 1955.
[20] *Financial Times*, 7 Nov. 1955.
[21] BAKELITE LTD., *Tech. Data Copper Clad Laminated for Printed Circuits.*
[22] *Financial Times*, 21 Sept. 1955, p. 9.
[23] T.C.C. LTD., *Special Products Bulletin* No. 2, London, Oct. 1954.
[24] DUMMER, G. W., JOHNSTON, D. L., *Electr. Engin.*, **25**, 309, Nov. 1953, 406–61.
[25] T.C.C. LTD., *Special Products Bulletin*, No. 3, London, Dec. 1954.
[26] BURGESS, E., *The Engineer*, **184**, 10 Oct. 1947, 332–3.
[27] CHAPMAN, C. L., *Elect. Engin.*, **25**, Oct. 1953, 309.
[28] ANON., *Machinery Lloyd*, *XXVI*, 9, 24 Apr. 1954.
[29] YARDNEY, M. S., *Jet Propulsion*, **25**, 9, Part II, Sept. 1955, 42S.
[30] HAMILTON STANDARD, *Data Sheet*, Windsor Locks, 1955.
[31] ANON., *Aero Digest*, **63**, 8, Nov. 1951, 88–98, 103.
[32] KOLLSMAN, *Advance Engineering Release*, M-72, 1,500–454, 1955.
[33] GECKLER, R. D., *Jet Propulsion*, **25**, 10, Oct. 1955, 540–41.
[34] GRASEBY INSTRUMENTS LTD., *Data Sheet* GW3, Tolworth, 1955.
[35] GYROMECHANISMS INC., *Data Sheet*, New York, 1955.
[36] MAZER, D. G., *Electronics*, **27**, 11, Nov. 1954, 164–7.
[37] BOWER, G. E., WYN, J. B. Jr., *Electronics*, **28**, 6, June 1955, 164–7.
[38] RIDDLE, F. D., *Electronics*, **27**, 1, Jan. 1954, 178–80.
[39] MINISTRY OF SUPPLY, *Press Release*, T.162523(s), Oct. 1953, see *Engineering*, **176**, 23 Oct. 1953, 518–19.
[40] SOMMERS, D. J., *Electronics*, **28**, 7, July 1955, 130–3.
[41] GERLACH, A. A., *Electronics*, **26**, 1, Jan. 1953, 108–11.

CHAPTER IV

TESTING AND TEST FACILITIES

◎

THE DEVELOPMENT of any guided missile is very different from that of a conventional aircraft. After an aircraft has been designed, the usual procedure is for a prototype to be built which can be flight-tested for many hours. Observations can be made by trained scientists and by the aircrew flying the aeroplane, leading to modifications which can be incorporated from time to time. Nearly all of these modifications can be made to the original aircraft on which their effects can be tested. With missiles on the other hand it is almost impossible to operate similarly. Essentially this is so because the missile is nearly always a one-shot vehicle. As a result it arises that a completely new missile must be built every time a modification has to be made to the design. When guided missiles began to be developed, therefore, many of the early programmes depended on the production and use of test vehicles. But of course this is a very expensive procedure, as it is necessary to fire large numbers of test vehicles during the development of any single missile. For example the Boeing BOMARC was developed after the firing of 100 GAPA test vehicles.[1] At the end of World War II there was moreover a scarcity of basic knowledge concerning missile structure, propulsion, and aerodynamics (especially the high-speed aerodynamics of flight at high Mach numbers as required by many missile designs). Consequently a great amount of basic scientific research had also to be carried out with the test vehicles in addition to engineering development. Much of this research could have been avoided had supersonic wind tunnels been available. But many countries including Britain had no such tunnels at the beginning of their guided missile programmes, and hence they had to rely entirely on rocket test vehicles.

An example of how supersonic data were quickly obtained is given by the NACA's pilotless aircraft research station at Wallops Island, Virginia.[2, 3] In 1945, just after World War II, before any supersonic wind tunnels were available, this research station was used for the conduction of investigations into the transonic and supersonic speed ranges, using for this purpose free-flight and rocket-propelled research models. Many varied and unusual aircraft shapes were tried, and the aerodynamic data obtained by radar tracking and radio telemetry during these tests were used for the design of high-speed missiles.

The Wallops Island NACA facilities were essentially an aero-dynamic range in which research covered such matters as lift, drag, stability, control effectiveness, damping in roll, missile stabilization, flutter buffeting, boundary layer phenomena, ramjet inlet and engine performance, and aerodynamic heating.

A bomb drop technique was first used for gathering data over the transonic regions. In this technique a research model was dropped over Wallops Island from a height of more than 30,000 ft (10,000 m) and the data were obtained by radar tracking and by telemeter. The force of gravity accelerated the model through the transonic speed range in its free fall to Earth. This method was developed as being the simplest and the quickest way of obtaining transonic data. In fact a similar experimental technique had been tried in Great Britain when rocket propelled models were dropped from aircraft and used both a falling and a rocket propulsion technique to achieve high velocities.[4] (*Fig.* 4.1.)

Two years later a rocket model technique for obtaining continuous data from subsonic speeds through the transonic range and far into the supersonic region was developed. (*Fig.* 4.2.) The rockets were launched from stands on the beach. After attaining a top speed of perhaps 1,500 m.p.h. (2,400 km/hr) the research model flew through the air with no propulsive force. Usually a booster rocket was employed to give rapid take-off and was jettisoned while a delayed fuse ignited the rocket charge embodied in the model. Alternatively other models relied solely upon the booster, and they carried no charges within themselves to sustain propulsion. For some tests a small research model was mounted on a balance projecting from the nose of the main rocket vehicle. The location of the model in space and its velocity at any time during the flight was determined by radar, while telemetering was used to give a record of the various aerodynamic reactions of the model as measured by instruments carried within it.

(a) *A free-falling missile which is used for aerodynamic studies and for testing high-speed parachutes. The spike on the nose prevents the missile from tumbling after it has landed nose first in the desert.*

(Photo. Cook Research Laboratories)

(b) *Successful recovery of a free-falling missile after a drop of nearly seven miles. Its descent was checked first by automatic dive brakes (seen open) and then by a parachute whose shroud lines can be seen leading away from the tail, the body is buried nose first in the sandy soil of the California desert. The model wings are undamaged and the instruments and the records they made during the fall can be recovered intact.* (Photo. N.A.C.A.)

Fig. 4.1

The trajectory carried the rocket models 5 to 10 miles (8 to 16 km) before they plunged into the sea. Altitudes attained were between 15,000 and 30,000 ft (5,000 to 10,000 m) though some models reached 100,000 ft (30,000 m). Top speed ranged from 15 to 40 miles per min (24 to 64 km per min), that is 2,400 m.p.h. (3,900 km/hr).

FIG. 4.2. *A rocket model with external booster which was used in research investigation concerning external stores mounted at the wind tips, a possible missile configuration.*

(Photo. N.A.C.A.)

During flight a model could be put through a series of controlled manœuvres. It could be made to roll, dive, climb and turn, thus exerting various forces on the control surfaces and the wings. The control mechanism was set for the desired programme before the take-off. The results obtained from a series of tests of this nature were of a great help in assessing manœuvrability and stability of the designs used.

For programmed manœuvres of missiles use is found of high pressure solenoid operated valves. One of these[5] weighs 8 oz (0·23 kg) and operates to control air pressures up to 130 atmospheres. When connected to the supply circuit a balance of pressure exists on either side of the main valve which is closed by a spring. The action of the solenoid allows one side of the valve to bleed to atmosphere and the resulting pressure differential opens the main valve. By this means rapid and positive operation is ensured. Once it is energized, the valve is held open by a retaining spring after removal of the supply voltage thus minimizing the drain on the missile's power supply.

The telemeter transmitted the readings given by numerous pressure pick-ups on the skin and by other instruments mounted inside the missile. It sent to the ground station a continuous record of acceleration, position of the aerodynamic controls, forces acting on the controls, aerodynamic forces acting on the model such as lift and drag, pressures acting on its surface and attitude in regard to the air stream.

Two radars were employed; a doppler velocity and a flight-path radar. Most of the records were made photographically on strip film at the ground station from the telemetered and the radar data. All results of the tests were thus recorded graphically on the same film, and could later be compared as functions of time and distance.

In order to study the stability and the control characteristics of bodies moving through the atmosphere the Newtonian equations of motion can be applied. On the one side they have force and moment terms while mass and inertia appear on the other. The latter can be evaluated by a suitable choice of reference axes, but the former consists of independent variables and combinations of independent variables contributing to the forces and to the moments. It has been found that experience is the most important factor in identifying the independent variables. Once this has been done approximations of the force and of the moment functions can be obtained by a Taylor's expansion of the variables and of their time derivatives.

However, no solutions to the general equations of motion exist, and to obtain working solutions either restricted cases must be considered or analogue and digital computers have to be used.

Aerodynamicists use the term *stability derivatives* for the force and moment derivatives with respect to the independent variables and their derivatives. It is possible to determine these experimentally by static or dynamic tests. In the former, which takes place in wind tunnels, one or more of the six degrees of freedom is restricted. Full-scale dynamic tests are expensive and time consuming, so dynamic tests with models are made in aero-ballistic ranges of which there are about half-a-dozen in operation. These ranges enable quick results to be obtained at a cost and on a time basis comparable to tests made in wind tunnels. (*Fig.* 4.3.)

The aero-ballistic range at the Canadian Armament Research and Development Establishment[6] consists of a building of concrete construction about 20 ft × 20 ft (6·1 m) × 760 ft (230 m) in length. One end is closed except for an inlet hole through which the models enter. The models themselves which are being tested are launched through a smooth-bore gun by means of a discarding sabot constructed of four petals. These open and sheer by air pressure after the sabot and the model have left the gun barrel. Scattering rapidly from the line of fire they are stopped from entering the ballistic range by a blast wall. (*Fig.* 4.4.)

Models tested have had wing spans of 5 in (12·7 cm), body lengths of 2 ft (61 cm), and have achieved velocities between 600 and 4,000 ft per sec (182 to 1,200 m/s).

The angular orientation of a model and its displacement from the line of fire is measured by yaw cards, of 9 ft × 12 ft (3 m × 4 m) in size. Special paper has to be used in order to obtain good signatures as the model passes through the cards. To identify roll one of the panels of the missile is marked with a blue dye which leaves a distinctive mark on each card.

At the Naval Ordnance Test Station Aero-ballistic Laboratory, at Inyokern, California, an electrical discharge of photo-flash lamps is used to provide micro-second duration illumination for photographing the rocket models in flight. The centre of gravity of each model is determined to within 0·001 ft (·304 mm) as far as the transverse component is concerned and to within 0·01 ft (3·04 mm) longitudinally. The time co-ordinate can be determined by this method to within 1 micro-second. The range itself is 500 ft (152 m) in length and the models are fired from 3 in and 40 mm guns and are photographed at intervals of 4 ft (1·22 m) during flight. To do this there are twenty-three pairs of precision ballistic cameras with overlapping fields of view for the adjacent pairs. Each camera photographs

FIG. 4.3. *Photograph of a missile model taken at Mach 2 under free flight conditions in an aeroballistic range.*

(Photo. C.A.R.D.E. Ref. 6)

the model six times to give 138 pairs of images during the complete flight. The flashes themselves are triggered by photo-cells and the source of power for the flashes comes from a bank of condensers. Although the last flash is slightly less bright than the first, this is not detrimental to the operation of the range. The velocities of flight vary between 800 and 6,000 ft per sec (240 to 1,800 m/s).[7]

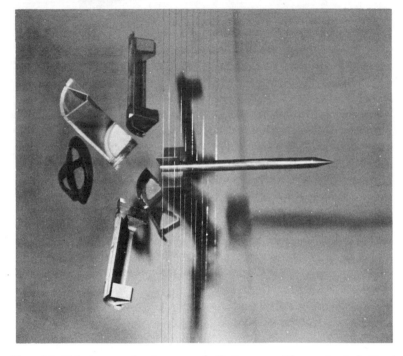

FIG. 4.4. *Sabot separation in an aeroballistic range. The carrier is built so that the air forces cause it to break into four petals after leaving the muzzle. The missile model is moving at Mach 2 and passing through the wires it triggers the flash which enabled the photograph to be taken.*
(Photo. C.A.R.D.E. Ref. 6)

A similar type of free-flight tunnel, 365 ft (111 m) in length, is available at Vernon and also uses high-intensity flash photography.[8]

An example of the type of supersonic wind tunnel (*Fig.* 4.5) now being used by many companies and government departments for investigation of guided weapon problems, is that constructed by the

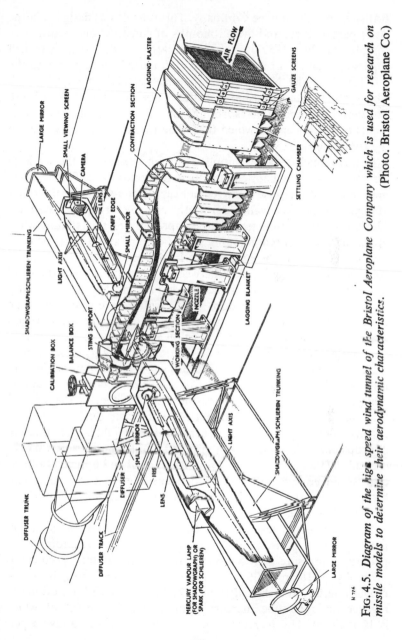

FIG. 4.5. *Diagram of the high speed wind tunnel of the Bristol Aeroplane Company which is used for research on missile models to determine their aerodynamic characteristics.*
(Photo. Bristol Aeroplane Co.)

British Bristol Aeroplane Company. This tunnel[9] was designed in the latter part of 1950, and fifteen months of constructional work were completed in June 1952. It is one of the largest of the privately owned supersonic tunnels in Great Britain and, indeed, second only to the 3-ft tunnel at the National Aeronautical Establishment, Bedford. The Bristol tunnel is unusual in its use of hot air as the working fluid. The designed speed range is from Mach 1·75 to 3·5, the speed increments being in steps of Mach 0·25. The tunnel can also be used in the transonic range.

In this tunnel the air is supplied at high pressure to the working system and is then exhausted directly to the atmosphere. This arrangement was made because a convenient supply of a vast quantity of air at high pressure was available from the near-by turbine test stations. The power absorption from the compressors of this station when operating at top speed amounts to 27,000 h.p. and a great proportion of the energy appears as heat in the air stream. This heat is conserved by lagging the duct between the test station and the wind tunnel buildings. The employment of hot air for the tunnel obviates cooling and drying installations which would have cost more than the tunnel itself for construction. When closed-circuit wind tunnels are used it is an economic proposition to dry the air because it is the same air being re-circulated all the time, but in this Bristol tunnel where the air is exhausted to the atmosphere it is much more economical and efficient to apply heat to the air. Either heating or drying must be used in order to reduce the water content of the air to a fraction at which condensation does not occur during the rapid expansion through the nozzle, otherwise there would be precipitation of droplets which would form a mist and lead to condensation shocks around the model under test. Moreover, visual and optical examination would be impaired and the condensation shock waves would form a false pattern of the normal pressure distribution around the model being tested.

To examine the test model's charactcristics three methods are used; pressure plots, strain gauging, and optical recording. The pattern of pressure distribution on the surface of the specimen is taken by 0·016 in (·406 mm) bore hypodermic tubing from the model interior, and thereafter by 0·25 in (6·35 mm) bore tubing to register on a 60-tube mercury manometer, the height of which is 10 ft (3 m). The mercury levels are photographed to give a per-

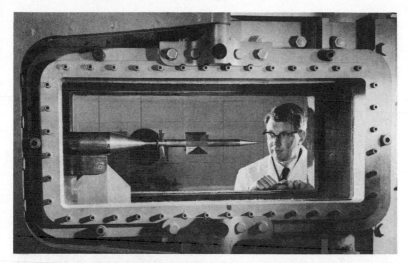

(a) *Dr. W. F. Hilton, Chief Aerodynamicist, inspects a model of a guided missile in the working section of the new Armstrong Whitworth supersonic wind tunnel.* (Photo. Armstrong Whitworth Ltd.)

(b) *The type of airflow near to the surface of this missile model in a super-sonic wind tunnel is shown clearly by ultra-violet light. The dark parts indicate that the flow is smooth or laminar; the lighter areas are regions of turbulent boundary layer flow. A luminescent lacquer is sprayed on to the model and it dries more rapidly where turbulent flow takes place. This model is in an airstream moving at Mach 2.* (Photo. N.A.C.A. Ames Aeronautical Lab.)

FIG. 4.6

(c) *Another method of studying airflow at high speeds and at low pressures depends upon what is known as an afterglow technique. With this method it is possible to study shock wave formation at the very low atmospheric densities which missiles would experience at extreme altitudes. Nitrogen is used in the wind tunnel instead of air and it is electrically charged so that it will glow, the intensity of the glow being maximum at the location of the shock waves. This model is being tested at Mach 3 in an atmosphere equivalent to an altitude of 30 miles.*

(Photo. N.A.C.A., Ames Aeronautical Lab.)

FIG. 4.6

manent record. The strain gauge technique is employed to register forces and moments imposed on the test model. However, as normal strain gauges would not have operated at the air flow temperatures involved, it was necessary for new types of gauges to be developed using a ceramic cement as a bonding agent. The readings of these strain gauges were permanently recorded by electronic pen chart recorders.

Shadowgraph and Schlieren apparatus are used for the third method of examination. These devices permit the shock wave formations and the boundary layer behaviour about the model to be photographed. Both systems work on the same basis, that is, that the fluctuating density in the air will cause shadows to be cast in a beam of parallel light. The arrangement of the shadowgraph is to pass a beam of this nature across the air stream so that a silhouette of the model is shown together with varying tone shadows of the flow discontinuities about it. The Schlieren apparatus uses a knife edge to give a much greater degree of contrast and detail in the resultant picture. Permanent records are again made photographically.

Because models are used in work of this nature it is necessary to have their shapes made within great degrees of accuracy. In the Bristol tunnel a general dimensional tolerance of less than 0·001 in (·025 mm) was found to be necessary, and the models were, indeed, made of high grade tensile steel.

An ingenious method of model support employs a sting which extends forward from a vertical quadrant down-stream of the working section. The sting is a solid bar of high tensile steel so made as to form a complex of spring flexures. The forces and moments are strain-gauge measured as spring deflexions in the sting.

In addition to wind tunnels which can be continuously operated there are also intermittent blow-down tunnels which give a short blast, but which reproduce for a short time conditions which could not be duplicated in a continuous tunnel. One installation of this type is operated by the Gas Dynamics Laboratory of the NACA. This is a wind tunnel which is used for studying the fundamental aspects of the problems of flight at very high speeds and great altitudes. Air at high pressures and elevated temperatures is required for this type of work; the high pressure being needed to give large scale effects while the temperatures are required to avoid air lique-faction at the high Mach numbers, and also so that heat transfer problems can be investigated. Heat transfer problems are of great importance when long-range ballistic missiles are considered as having to re-enter the upper atmosphere at tremendous velocities.

At the Gas Dynamics Laboratory clean dry air is stored in a tank farm consisting of a large number of steel bottles which can store 20,000 cu ft (560 cu m) of air under a pressure of 33 atmospheres. Special heating devices can bring this air to a temperature of just over 540° C before it is applied to the wind tunnel. In this tunnel altitude of up to 200,000 ft (61,000 m) can be simulated, and speeds of up to nine times that of sound obtained.[10]

Even though nowadays there are many electronic aids—such as

electronic simulators—to the design of missiles, in the final analysis a live guided missile must be fired. (*Fig.* 4.7.) Moreover, live missiles have to be shot to enable personnel to be trained in their efficient operation. Accordingly, there are in various parts of the world a

FIG. 4.7(a) *The launching of a V-2 research missile at White Sands Proving Grounds, New Mexico, as seen from the interior of the control blockhouse.*
(Photo. General Electric Company)

number of missile test ranges. In the United States, for example, the Air Force has a Missile Test Centre at Patrick Air Force Base, Cocoa, Florida[11] and another Missile Test Centre at Holloman Air Force Base in New Mexico.[12] The U.S. Navy has a Missile Test Centre at Point Mugu, California, an Ordnance Test Station at

Fig. 4.7 (*b*) *An aerodynamic research model by the Fairey Aviation Company and used to investigate the problems associated with vertical take-off interceptors, moves away from its launching platform at Woomera. The zebra sticks are used to measure the acceleration of guided missiles and research vehicles.*

(Photo. L.R.W.E. Salisbury)

Inyokern, California,[13] and an Ordnance Missile Test Facility at White Sands Proving Ground, New Mexico. The U.S. Army has the White Sands Proving Grounds[14] and test facilities also at Redstone Arsenal. In addition there are a number of test stations where specific components such as propulsion units are tested. Missile test stations in the Soviet Union include those at Tomsk, Kronstadt, Insel, Stalingrad, Ost, Ust-Urt, Kara-Kum, Uralskoje and at Peenemünde in Eastern Germany.

In the case of Britain there is the proving ground at Aberporth on Cardigan Bay, in Wales, and now a new proving ground in the Hebrides, while the main missile testing centre is at Woomera in Central Australia. (*Fig. 4.7 (b).*)

Indeed, a tremendous amount of work is at present being done by Britain and Australia and it is reported that more than 2,000 test missiles had been fired at the rocket ranges at Woomera and Aberporth up to 1955. The Australian testing ground for guided weapons[15] is about 270 miles (430 km) north-west of Adelaide and 9 miles (14 km) from Timba a small township on the trans-continental railway.

The site was selected because it provides a land range of some 1,250 miles (2,000 km). This is the longest land range in the world, stretching from Woomera over a very sparsely populated area to the coast of Western Australia.

The base headquarters for guided weapon work is at Salisbury and is accommodated in a modern establishment which had been built during World War II as an explosives factory. It is a policy to carry out as much engineering as possible at Salisbury and to use the range at Woomera only for the essential work connected with the carrying out of the trials.

Woomera, which is an aboriginal name for throwing stick, is built on what is known locally as 'gibber' country in which the vegetation is generally limited to a hardy salt bush. The country was used for sheep grazing but, because of the poor quality of the soil, it had a carrying capacity of only about one sheep to every ten acres.

A modern township has now been built on the site to provide all the amenities needed for comfortable living. An adequate shopping centre has also been provided together with an up-to-date hospital and a school. The population of between 3,000 and 5,000 people resides in 500 houses of brick or pre-fabricated construction and in extensive single quarters.

The area has a very low rainfall and practically no natural supplies of water. For this reason it was necessary to lay approximately 100 miles (160 km) of pipeline in order to connect the township to the River Murray Whyalla water supply.

An American range for the testing of long-range missiles is the Air Force Missile Test Centre at Cocoa, Florida, extending for 1,000 miles (1,600 km) over the Atlantic Ocean. (*Fig.* 4.8.) For each test firing over 400 men stand by to man the recording instruments in a chain of observing stations on the Caribbean Islands, all linked by timing signals from an automatic master clock at the control base.

At Cape Canaveral, where the launching pads are situated, there is a concrete blockhouse equipped with periscope-like observation posts. Three miles distant is the central control building with its tracking and search radars. Inside this building the path of the missile is displayed on visual trackers so that the range-safety officer can destroy it by radio if it strays off course. The launching phase is recorded by over a score of special cameras.

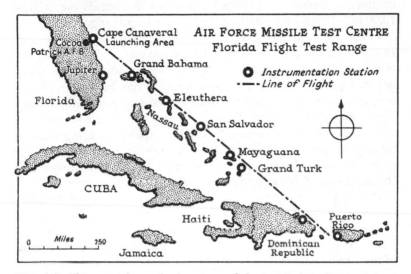

FIG. 4.8. *This map shows the locations of the instrumentation stations on islands reaching across the Caribbean from Florida to Puerto Rico. Radar and other electronic methods are used to guide the missiles during their flight and the path of a typical test is shown by the dotted line extending from the launching pad at Cape Canaveral 500 miles across the ocean.*

(Photo. U.S. Information Service)

Radar aerials are placed along the route in the various islands and the surrounding ocean to cover the pre-determined track along which the missile is expected to fly. Optical devices are also used to measure angles and to give further details for the computation of missile speed and its exact course. At control base tape recorders store the signals received from the telemetering gear within the missile.

This American range has greater possibilities because it may be extended to take the firing of missiles out over the South Atlantic even as far as the Antarctic. This will be essential, of course, for the testing of long-range intercontinental ballistic missiles. Indeed in January 1956 it was announced that by agreements between the United States and Britain, the chain of radar and optical tracking stations associated with the range will be extended a further 500 miles (800 km) by installations on the British Island of St. Lucia. It was reported that this was needed for the flight testing of the inter-continental SNARK missile, the range of which exceeds the original 1,000 mile (1,600 km) length of the Caribbean proving area.*

In the previous chapter it was shown how telemetry can be used to send data from the missile to the ground station. These data are, of course, coded, and the code, together with methods for its trans-lation, vary with different organizations. It has been pointed out, too, that the way in which the code can be impressed on the radio signals may also be varied. But the essential of all these telemetering systems is that the decoding should be capable of being done as quickly as possible in order that the missile engineers and the designers can evaluate the tests and make their modifications with the minimum of delay to the missile development programme.

During the early stages of missile development, signal decoding was a very laborious task, but in recent years many electronic de-vices have been designed to ease the work. An example of the diffi-culties besetting early workers is shown by reference to the beginning of the Boeing guided missile programme. It was found, for example, that more than 1,000 man-hours were expended in processing the facts gathered from a single minute of flight of the BOMARC ground-to-air missile. But as new electro-mechanical systems were developed this time was shortened to one twentieth of the original period. One system developed by Boeing[16] relied upon messages from the missile being recorded on a plastic tape (*Fig.* 4.9) which then passes through a data recorder. This sends electrical impulses to magnetized needles which write the data down in a series of numbers on specially pre-pared paper. The paper is in the form of rolls, similar to adding machine tally rolls, but it turns black wherever the electric needle allows a spark to pass through it. From one minute of flight so much data are received that 600 ft (183 m) of this paper are needed to record them.

The carbonized markings on the paper represent the numbers telemetered by the guided missile from just prior to launching until its final plunge to destruction far away in the Atlantic Ocean. The numbers are, in fact, in binary terms, and while these can be decoded

*By agreement in June 1956 between the U.S. and British Governments the range is to be extended to 3,000 miles (4,800 km) and will end at Ascension Island.

laboriously by a human operator, it is much less time consuming to place the decoding into the hands of a machine. One black dot on the paper stands for the number one. The absence of a mark on the paper indicates zero. These are the only two numbers employed in this binary system but in varying combinations they may also be

FIG. 4.9. Six hundred feet of paper tape are used to record the information received from 1 min of flight of the Bomarc missile. Numbers in the binary system are represented by black dots on the tape and a data converting system reads the dots by passing over them with electro-sensitive brushes.

(Photo. Boeing Airplane Company)

used to represent any number in the normal decimal system. Alone they can indicate many happenings which only need to be recorded as on or off. There are quite a number of such factors in guided missile work; for example, valves open or closed, switches on or off, electronic instruments operating or not operating. All these are recorded at the ground station by the presence or absence of the black dots on the recording paper roll.

A data converting machine is used to read binary-coded rolls and transfer the data to punched cards. After conversion into the decimal system the data are then fed into computing machines which automatically allow for errors which may have occurred during transmission, taking into consideration pre-flight conditions and the special peculiarities of the individual experiment. The information is then passed on to a machine which plots the data as a series of graphs. These, of course, are in conventional form such as propellant-feed pressure against time, altitude, yaw, etc., and they can be readily studied. The designer uses them to appraise the results of the telemetered data taken in conjunction with films of the tests and still photographs exposed all along the path followed by the missile. There are also the other data recorded by the various ground stations, for example the radar plots, which have all to be correlated with that transmitted from the missile itself.

During flight, of course, the data have to be gathered within the missile and a number of new instruments have been designed for this purpose, for example, pressure transducers which are used for measuring pressures such as those experienced in propellant lines and tanks. Often these incorporate a bourdon tube which operates the brush of a precision potentiometer. Such types are unaffected by severe vibration and acceleration and can measure pressures up to 3,000 atmospheres.

Pressure can also be measured by resistance pressure gauges. Essentially these consist of a thin-walled steel tube, to the inside of which the pressure is applied. Around the tube is wound a non-inductive helix of fine resistance wire. The pressure expands the tube slightly and in doing so it stretches the wire, thereby increasing its resistance. This adaptation of the strain-gauge principle gives a useful method of pressure measurement and has, of course, a small physical size. Moreover, by using such an instrument in the propellant lines it is possible to measure propellant-feed pressure without disturbing the flow in any way; both pulsating and steady conditions being easily recorded by suitable choice of measuring circuits.

The opening of propellant valves can also be determined by causing the valve to change the capacity of a condenser as it opens. The time of valve lift is then indicated with great accuracy.

Measurements of the acceleration of missiles are also very important, especially if a pre-set programme has been arranged for the test vehicle, in which various rates of acceleration have to be followed accurately. Indeed with missile control it has already been pointed out that it is essential that the missile should not merely move either, say, to right or to the left, but that it should move at some definite and accurately determined rate of acceleration. Accelerometers therefore find extensive application in most missile instrumentations. These can be in several forms. One accelerometer[17] consists of a condenser-type pick-up and relies upon a supported mass, damped by a silicone fluid, suspended by a spider which restricts movement to one degree of freedom. A condenser diaphragm is actuated by the motion of the supported mass so that the variation in capacity will give a measure of the acceleration being experienced by the instrument. Accelerations up to 500 times that of gravity can be measured with an instrument of this kind.

Most linear accelerometers measure acceleration similarly by the movement of a spring-supported mass system which actuates the brush of a potentiometer or changes the value of a capacity or of an inductance. The resistance ratio is proportional to the magnitude of the acceleration. These accelerometers are small and robust in construction and have a relatively high natural frequency. They may have a linearity of $\pm$ 1 per cent, a resolution of 0·25 per cent and weigh less than 1 lb (0·5 kg). They will take a current of only about 10 milliamps for their operation.[18]

Accelerometers like these can be used to measure either longitudinal or transverse accelerations up to one hundred times that of gravity. Graseby Instruments Ltd. produce an accelerometer which is complete with driving unit and time-base mechanism. It produces a 34-sec record of linear acceleration against a time base. It is liquid damped and consists of a spring-supported mass restricted to one degree of freedom. Recording is effected by means of a stylus which provides a trace on a transparent plastic strip which is secured to the periphery of a recording drum, which itself is driven by clockwork. Starting can either be electrically or by the operation of an inertia switch. Alternatively a potentiometer can be attached to give a pick-up for telemetering.

Often in the case of missiles it is advantageous to use strain-gauge amplifiers having transistors, because this method is particularly desirable for remote instrumentation where space and power are limiting factors. At present, however, the required degree of stability has only been obtained with a.c. strain-gauge amplifiers. Transistorization of d.c. amplifiers still appears to present several major obstacles.

The first test vehicles used for guided missile development in Britain appeared in 1946, when the LOP-GAP project originated at Farnborough. This test vehicle used propellants of liquid oxygen and a water diluted methyl alcohol. Gas pressure from a slow-burning cordite cartridge forced a piston against propellants to expel them from their tanks. The earliest rocket test vehicles were launched without any radio control and were used merely to determine the aerodynamic stability and to test the effectiveness of the booster rockets. As has been pointed out, this separation proved to be a very difficult problem in the early rocket tests. A number of early British RTVs abandoned the tandem arrangement and overcame the difficulty by substituting a wrap-around booster which separated by air pressure on its release.

Any guided missile can be regarded as consisting of three major systems; first the airframe, second the propulsion unit, and third the guidance. In addition there is the warhead and its arming and detonating equipment. Each of these separate systems must be thoroughly tested for compatibility with the others. This is because it has been found that all sections of a missile and its system react violently on each other. Guided missile development has, indeed, demanded that a number of new techniques for the testing of components should be developed. Components are evaluated by being given exhaustive tests to see how they react to shock, vibration, heat, cold, high humidity, high and low voltages, storage, acceleration, altitudes and low pressures. After individual checking the components have then to be checked as part of the missile in order to ensure compatibility. Environmental test laboratories are needed which have centrifuges, altitude chambers, shake devices, and impact testers. These devices submit the missiles and their components to every conceivable condition of altitude, temperature, pressure, humidity, impact, vibration and acceleration. Every component which goes into a guided missile must be tested to ensure that it meets the specification within very close tolerances.

All defence missiles have to be capable of high accelerations, laterally as well as longitudinally and sometimes to as high as 20 Gs. An example of a centrifugal testing instrument is that developed by Graseby Instruments Ltd.,[19] in conjunction with the Royal

Aircraft Establishment at Farnborough. This uses a light-weight table which can be employed to test components weighing up to 12 lb (5·4 kg) and between accelerations of one quarter and one hundred times that of gravity. Speed control is by a hybrid circuit which operates by comparing the output voltage of a tach-generator with a pre-set proportion of the voltage of a reference battery,

FIG. 4.10. *A centrifugal testing machine for guided missile components.*
(Photo. Graseby Instruments Ltd.)

amplifying the difference and using this amplified signal to control the resistance of a carbon pile which regulates the voltage supplied to the armature of the driving motor. This circuit controls the speed to within 0·25 per cent. Facilities are provided for making connexions to electrically-operated and air-operated components while they are on the centrifuge. (*Fig.* 4.10.)

The importance of pre-flight and pre-installation checks is nowhere brought out so clearly as it is with electronic valves. Interesting data have been published of experience by North American Aviation in this field.[20] Of 33,000 radio valves inspected, 2,600 had to be rejected outright after electrical tests, but of the remainder a large number showed mechanical flaws which might have proved to be detrimental if they had been used in guided missile work. Examples included sloping bands in miniature tubes, partly melted structural members, poor bonds between wires and leads, and cutting of grid turns during assembly. Valves were examined by microscope and by X-rays for internal flaws in the electrode assembly and by polariscopic devices for strains in the glass envelope. To January 1954 the test programme at North American Aviation gave 66 per cent perfect valves, 26 per cent with assembly irregularities, and 8 per cent electrical rejects. Only the highest quality valves were colour-coded for use in critical installations.

Data were, however, passed back to the valve manufacturers and it was found that as the test programme continued the number of rejects decreased. Indeed, one type of subminiature valve gave a yield of 80 per cent suitable for use in critical installations. Arising from the programme it was found that X-ray inspection revealed the same percentage of additional irregularities as did the original visual microscopic examination.

In free flight tests methods of tracking the missiles are essential; these fall into two classes, optical groups, which include telescopes and cameras, and electronic devices such as telemetry, which has already been discussed, and radar Doppler. The aim of the tracking device is to pin-point the location of the missile in three dimensions at each instant during its flight. At the same time the acceleration, the speed and the attitude must be known. Telemetry attends to some of these things, for example, acceleration and attitude, and in addition telemetry gives information concerning the performance of the components; pumps, servomechanisms and ejection devices. But the tracking equipment must be relied upon to give the exact location of the missile and can also be used for checking the attitude. At White Sands Proving Grounds, for example, the missile's position is plotted at half-second intervals, which in a flight lasting for two minutes means that 250 points are determined. The tracking of an air-to-air missile is naturally a very different matter from that of an intercontinental ballistic missile. In the former case it would be quite feasible to have a camera in an aircraft, one in the missile, and also one in the target drone. Taken in conjunction with ground radar these three cameras would give all the necessary information for the determination of the test parameters. However, in the case of an intercontinental ballistic missile, a chain of radar stations is required. It has been shown that the long-range weapons proving range at Cocoa has facilities for this type of test.

A typical test of a high-altitude rocket[21] at White Sands would begin with ribbon-frame motion picture cameras photographing the ascent in a series of thin pictures side by side on a strip of film. Ballistic cameras would then make a series of exposures in quick succession all on the same plate. As the missile ascends farther, search radar plots its course on maps of the range so that the range-safety officers can ensure that it is not going to fall in any populated area. Telescopes are also used to track the path and these have attached to them high-speed movie cameras which show the orientation of the rocket at all times. It is necessary that all these optical tracking devices should be synchronized with the other data received by the telemetry system. Accordingly a time signal is usually synchronized and placed on the optical record. For the lowest altitudes an Askania photo-theodolite is used. This has a range of 30 or 40 miles (50 70 km) and is extremely accurate; some of the most recent models being accurate to within 6 sec of arc. For higher altitudes special tracking telescopes are used, which can keep the missile under observation to a height of nearly 200 miles (300 km). With the tracking telescope the step separation of multi-stage rockets can be observed, while any ejection of equipment, air break-up, attitude of the missile, and the behaviour of the jet exhaust can also be studied.

The failing with all optical equipment, of course, is that it can only be used under good weather conditions, the presence of even thin cloud layers renders this type of equipment inoperative. The radar tracking equipment may work at a wavelength of about 10 cm, and can follow the missile despite cloudy conditions. With its aid a trajectory can be calculated quickly but not with great accuracy. Accordingly the main use of radar tracking is to check the course of the missile for range safety purposes. The Doppler radio, on the other hand, does give improved accuracy compared with search radar. A continuous wave system is transmitted, the signals being radiated to the missile where the frequency is doubled and the signals re-radiated.

The relative velocity between the missile and the ground station produces a change in frequency which is a function of the missile's speed. At the ground station the returned signals are mixed with a control frequency coming directly from the transmitter, the resultant beats being a basis for calculating the speed of the missile. From the results of several such Doppler stations it is possible to determine both the acceleration and the position of the missile in space at each instant. The Doppler radio is a very accurate device and can give the change in position of the missile up to a distance of 100 miles (160 km) with an accuracy of about 6 in (15 cm). The failing is that it measures the change of position more accurately than the actual position relative to the ground station.

After the testing of missile configurations, of aerodynamic forces and of heat transfer effects over the whole vehicle, the next important range of test equipment is in connexion with the propulsive engine. Facilities for testing turbo-jets have been generally available in the aircraft industry for some time, but for the new ramjets and the rocket motors it was necessary to construct entirely new forms of engine test facilities.

The largest privately operated supersonic high altitude laboratory in the United States for the development and production testing of ramjet engines has been put in operation by the Wright Aeronautical Division of the Curtiss-Wright Corporation.[22] (*Fig.* 4.11.)

In an earlier chapter it was shown that ramjet engines are high-speed power plants which burn fuel and obtain the large amount of oxygen necessary for combustion through a front inlet into which air is rammed by the fast forward speed of the missile. The new laboratory, which cost over £2 million, was designed by Curtiss-Wright engineers and built under the sponsorship of the United States Air Force. It stands next to an earlier ramjet laboratory which was completed in 1949, and also close to the Government-sponsored Turbine Development Laboratory (constructed in 1946). The Ramjet facility will be able to test ramjets of huge size to high Mach numbers and at simulated altitudes from sea level to many thousands of feet. Although this test facility can be operated steadily for periods of more than one hour at a time, it can also run on a blow-down basis for 60 sec with the extremely high rate of air flow of 700 lb per sec (318 kg/s).

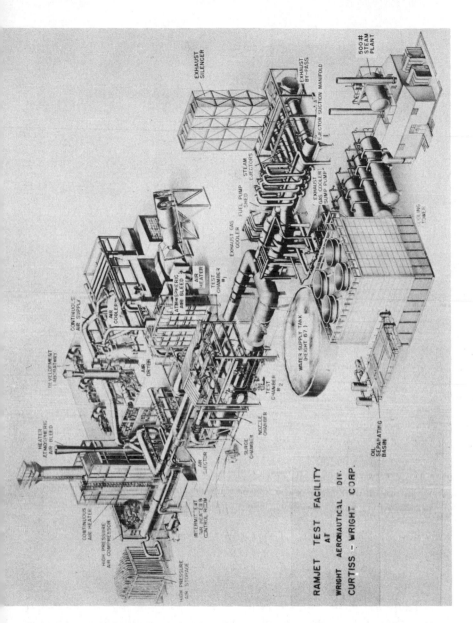

FIG. 4.11. *The ramjet test facility of the Curtiss-Wright Corporation which
can test ramjet propulsion plants on a ducted or free flow basis.*

(Photo. Curtiss-Wright Corporation)

121

The laboratory is also designed so that complete engines or components can be tested, and work can be done either on a ducted or a free jet basis.

What is reported to be America's largest aerodynamic and engine test facility is in final stages of construction in Tennessee, being the Arnold Engineering Development Centre of the United States Air Force Air Research and Development Command. The test centre has no less than seven wind tunnels and can duplicate conditions at speeds of up to Mach 10. There are also six engine test cells where altitudes of up to 100,000 ft (30,000 m) can be simulated, while in the gas dynamics facility hypersonic wind tunnels have cross sections up to 50 in (139 cm) in diameter, some being designed for continuous operation and others having intermittent air flows.

Air heated to a temperature of 820° C is used in the tunnels in order to prevent the air from liquefying as it cools by expansion through the hypersonic nozzles needed to give flow at high Mach numbers. It was at this Facility that the Hughes FALCON air-to-air missile and the ramjet propulsion plants of the Boeing BOMARC were originally tested.[23]

Analysis of the data gathered is by a number of Remington Rand Univac computers and data reduction systems. They can give the data either in printed tabular form or drawn as graphs plotted against *XY* axes.

Expensive and complex test pits are needed for rocket motor testing because of the serious hazards of fire and explosion, especially with new designs or with previously untried propellant combinations. Operators have to be protected by concrete-walled blockhouses, and all control of the unit should be remote, with safety devices to prevent accidental firings.[24] Automatic sprinkler systems have to be incorporated to extinguish fires and dilute spilled propellants.

In addition to the spectacular firing tests, a large number of tests must be made on each component part, because rocket motors are usually engines in which all the components are run at extreme conditions.[25] Such things as pumps and valves and ejectors have to be separately tested, usually first with water and then with the liquids which they will have to handle in the complete unit. Good ideas of the behaviour of components can be obtained from these water tests, but the final proving can only come from an actual firing. Honeycomb cans have been employed by some experimenters in order to ascertain the density of spray across a combustion chamber. Use was made of different liquids to represent the fuel and the oxidizer and their proportions were analysed in each of these cells.

Firing tests are made—usually observing the rocket through periscopes or by means of a closed television circuit—to determine if the engine starts smoothly, to see how it runs and the look of the exhaust flame. Having established that the motor does run and that it will continue to do so for some time, the next stage in testing is to find out the thrust, chamber pressure, the specific impulse developed and other quantitative information. These data are obtained from instruments arranged on the test bed or within the rocket motor. Banks of meters record the instrument readings and are photographed with a ciné camera along with time impulses. When transient effects are desired to be recorded, for example, high frequency oscillations of combustion chamber pressure, the normal gauges do not respond quickly enough, so that pressure-sensitive electrical pick-ups have to be used, together with a cathode-ray oscilloscope and a high-speed recording camera.

Pressure pick-ups are usually variable-capacity types, operating as frequency modulators or as an arm of a Wheatstone bridge. They can respond to transient phenomena at 50 kc/s if sufficiently high-speed continuous film cameras can be used. Temperatures are measured in a variety of ways; by thermocouples, by optical pyrometers, and by line-reversal spectroscopic methods. Flow rate of the propellants is ascertained by having devices in the feed lines such as steel balls, vanes or variable inductance cores, which can either alter the frequency of an oscillatory circuit or be counted as a system of changes, each being calibrated to give propellant flow rate.

In all tests the timing sequences are important, and it is wise to programme the firing so that operations take place automatically in an invariable sequence which will not permit subsequent operations to be completed should failure occur at any stage in the test. The timing devices should also operate the starting of the high-speed recording cameras and should return the test pit to safety conditions at the end of firing or if an emergency stop button is depressed.

An example of a rocket test facility of this nature is the Naval Air Rocket Test Station at Lake Denmark, New Jersey.[26] This facility consists primarily of the basic test stand, surrounded by outside propellant storage tanks, a guard house, a control house, and a network of drives and ramps. The buildings of the facility are set into a very steep slope some 400 ft (122 m) above the main highway, while the test stand itself (*Fig.* 4.12) is a massive structure of steel and concrete set into the side of a hill overlooking Lake Denmark. It is constructed in a cantilever fashion in the form of a steel framework covered with corrugated steel sheets with the actual test floor 50 to 70 ft (15 to 21 m) above ground level. Inside the stand is a

FIG. 4.12. *A typical rocket test stand is shown in this photograph of the NARTS E-1 installation at Lake Denmark, New Jersey.*

(Photo. Reaction Motors Inc.)

basement, a ground floor level, and the upper working floor. The lower floors house the propellant-tank rooms, while the upper floor consists of one large working room nearly 100 ft (30 m) long. This has a rolled-back type of roof so that large missile tank sections can be erected within it. The thrust load rating of the stand is about 175 tons, but the basic structure is stressed for even higher values than that.

The control house stands some 250 ft (80 m) away from the test stand. Within it are contained recording oscillographs, potentio-meters, ammeters, voltmeters, panels and plugs, lining the four walls and designed to record all the various parameters which have to be measured during the firing of a rocket engine. Visual observations of any test can be made through one of four viewing mirrors mounted directly over the control panels.

There are other large rocket test stands in various parts of the United States, one of which is the Malta Test Station.[27] This was associated with Project Hermes of the General Electric Company and the stand can accommodate rocket motors ranging from micro size—used for the testing of new propellant combinations—to long-range vehicle power plants having thrusts of up to 75 tons.

At Edwards Air Force Base in California, overlooking the Mojave Desert, are the largest rocket test stands of the United States Air Force[28, 29] (*Fig.* 4.13). This site was chosen as early as 1947, and the design and the installation was undertaken by the Aerojet Engineering Corporation. Construction began in 1949 and by July 1952 the first rocket motors were being tested. The stands are essentially of mono-lith construction with side bays for storing the propellants, and the working platform is cantilevered, jutting out near to the top of the stand, several storeys high. It is on this cantilevered platform that the motor and the tanks, with their associated pipes and controls, are mounted. The flame from the rocket motor under test is sent ver-tically downwards into a special flame pit below the test section. In this pit the rocket jet spalls the concrete, and in order to minimize damage, nozzles spray water at the rate of 4,000 gal (18,000 l) a min-ute to wash any corrosive propellants into the valley below. Again in the test shops associated with the stands, as in the Lake Denmark Facility, covering is by corrugated sheets of steel. The idea of a structure of this type is to produce a building which will fail partially in the event of an explosion. The main damage then is merely the thrusting aside of the sheets, whereas the skeleton structure itself is left undamaged.

The largest static test stand for complete missiles is situated at the Redstone Arsenal, Alabama. It is about 150 ft (50 m) high and can be used for the static testing of the projected intermediate range ballistic missile.

FIG. 4.13. *This photograph shows the use of graphic recorders and an observation periscope in the control blockhouse associated with the U.S. Air Force static test stands for liquid propellant rocket engines at Edwards Air Force Base.*   (Photo. U.S. Air Force)

Observation of tests and control of their operation is made from a control room fabricated with thick concrete walls and blast-proof shields. From this protection observers can operate the firing circuits and all the recording and observation equipment. As with most rocket test stations, special warning light systems are used and stringent safety precautions are observed. Sometimes television is used for direct observation of firing and of the flame pattern.

With all these test facilities there is the great problem of data reduction; that is, the taking of a large quantity of raw information, re-arranging it, and interpreting it by mathematical equations, so that a valid mathematical description of the performance is obtained.

The most important device for the analysis of this information is the electronic computer. With it the data can be reduced both economically and within a short space of time, so that it can be used in the practical design of modifications for the missile which has been tested. In some cases—for example the testing of a power plant or control system—it is essential that a large proportion, if not all, of the performance data should be available during the test itself, so that it can be fed back through servo controls to modify certain parameters during the continuance of the test. Only by using electronic computers to close the loop can this be possible, human operators are not quick enough.

On the other hand, in the case of a free flight the data can often be analysed at the convenience of the designers. Even so, with any missile, there is such a tremendous amount of data gathered in the space of a few minutes of flight, that it would take men working with normal calculating machines many weeks to sort out all the information from the firing of a single test round. With the aid of electronic computers, however, the process is speeded up considerably.

There are two types of computers employed in guided missile work; analogue computers and digital computers. The analogue describes either electrically or mechanically the operation of a certain physical situation. This type of computer can add, subtract, multiply, divide, integrate, and make changes in algebraic signs, and it is used extensively for the solution of problems in dynamics, as it is suitable for operations involving differential equations. The accuracy, however, cannot be greater than 98 per cent.

Digital computers, on the other hand, are much more accurate. Data is supplied to them in the form of a code, for example, on punched cards or tape or on magnetic tape, and the accuracy with which the computer deals with these data is limited only by the size of its storage bank systems. A digital computer, however, only performs one operation at a time, but it can perform this operation at a fantastic speed. A computer of the University of Manchester, for example, can give the sum of the squares of all numbers from 1 to 10,000 in about 60 seconds. Accordingly they serve best where there has to be repeated evaluations of complicated equations so that a loop system of computation can be employed. One of the great problems with all computers is getting the data into them fast enough. A method of solving this is to use high-speed tape readers on which the characters are impressed as punched holes in paper tape. It is usual to use the binary system where the presence or absence of any of five holes in a line can represent up to thirty-two characters, such as numbers from 1 to 9, instructions, decimal points, letters of the alphabet etc. Photo-electric cells are actuated when the light passes through the holes in the tape. Machines of this nature can read as many as 200 characters every second and feed these data on to the computer's storage banks.

One of Remington Rand's data processing systems is the Univac Scientific;[30] twelve of these machines are being used for highly classified applications in connexion with the defence industries. Several have been installed for processing guided missile data while the models are under test at the Arnold Engineering Development Centre. Another installation is at the White Sands Proving Grounds, New Mexico, and has played a vital role in the military guided missile development programme. Data on punched tape are fed into the Univac and come out in a final printed form. The data are originally gathered on radar scanners and from other devices at the various observation stations throughout the range.

A large amount of data is stored in these machines for use when required by recording and banking it externally on drums of magnetic tape. Alternatively it can be retained within the computer in a cylinder of mercury which is known as a mercury memory tank, or as spots of light on cathode ray tubes. In addition magnetic drums store thousands of items of information on their magnetized surfaces. They revolve continuously so that the items can be picked off again when they are required by the computer. Yet another method is what is known as magnetic core storage.

When the computer has processed its information ready for delivery, the results have to be converted into a printed form and this is accomplished by high-speed printing devices some of which can produce 600 lines of 130 characters each minute.

Photographic records of missile firings have to be analysed in order to produce information concerning both the trajectory and the attitude. Aerodynamic and control problems can then be resolved. One method of such analysis developed by the Telecomputing Corporation, California, uses projected images magnified up to 45 diameters. Measurements are made by an angle-measuring unit or by horizontal and vertical crosswires, the positions of which are accurately determined and converted to electrical impulses. The digital information is processed through an electronic computer, constants are added, and it is then permanently recorded in the form of punched cards, perforated tape or typewritten tabulated lists. Means are also provided for the tape or cards to be fed into equipment which plots the information against cartesian co-ordinates.

In Britain perhaps the best known example of computer work in connexion with guided missiles is the Tridac three-dimensional analogue computer at the Royal Aircraft Establishment, Farnborough.[31] This is one of the biggest computers in the world and takes 6,000 sq ft (560 sq m) of floor space. It uses 8,000 radio valves and consumes 650 kilowatts of electricity for its operation. With Tridac the operation of an entire missile can be simulated, also it is able to simulate the interception of a bomber by the missile. Positions of both vehicles are continuously displayed and their manœuvres are calculated by the computer. The Tridac operates in real time, that is, all the calculations are made at the same rate as that at which the events would occur in a real interception. This means that parts of missiles can be connected into the computer and tested individually as though they were part of an actual missile.[32] Agwac is a smaller version of Tridac which has been installed at the long-range weapons establishment in Australia. Analogue computers of this nature make it possible to test missiles without going to the tremendous expense of firing a live round. With their aid the development of missiles has been considerably speeded up so that several models are being manufactured or are now almost ready to go into production.

Countries like Britain where an early radar warning is not possible have had to concentrate on producing anti-aircraft devices which can enable interception to be made as far as possible from the target areas. Britain's missile which is now in production is accordingly an air-to-air missile for the destruction of invading bombers away from the coast line.

The United States, on the other hand, have the short-range NIKE ground-to-air interceptor, the FALCON air-to-air interceptor, and the MATADOR, REGULUS, CORPORAL, and HONEST JOHN, surface-to-surface tactical weapons in production and many other missiles in the course of development. In addition, concentration is being given to the production of long-range intercontinental strategic missiles which can act as a deterrent to any aggressors.

REFERENCES

[1] ANON., *Aviation Week*, **58**, 5, 2 Feb. 1953, 32–33, 35.
[2] NACA, *Press Release*, Washington, 1 May 1951.
[3] ANON., *Aviation Week*, **54**, 22, 28 May 1951, 19–20.
[4] SWAN, J., *et al. Aeron. Res. Counc. Rep. & Memo.* 2,835, 1954.
[5] GRASEBY INSTRUMENTS LTD., *Data Sheet* GW2, Tolworth, 1955.
[6] BULL, G. V., *C.A.R.D.E. Misc. Report*, 53/55, May 1955.
[7] BARKOFSKY, E., HOPKINS, R., DAWSICK, S., *Electronics*, **26**, 6, June 1953, 142–7.
[8] CARRIERE, P., *Inter Avia*, **10**, 5, May 1955, 331–3.
[9] BRISTOL AEROPLANE CO. LTD., *Press Release*, 1954.
[10] NACA *Inspection*, Langley Aeron. Laboratory, 1953.
[11] ANON., *Jet Propulsion*, **24**, 3, May–June 1954, 192–3.
[12] ANON., *Jet Propulsion*, **25**, 4, Apr. 1955, 178.
[13] ANON., *Jet Propulsion*, **25**, 8, Aug. 1955, 402–3.
[14] ANON., *Jet Propulsion*, **24**, 5, Sept.–Oct. 1954, 326–7.
[15] MCBRIDE, P. A., *priv. commun.*, July 1955.
[16] CALKINS, K., *Boeing Magazine*, **35**, 2, Feb. 1954, 3–5.
[17] CAMBERLEY INSTRUMENTS LTD., *Data Sheet*.
[18] GRASEBY INSTRUMENTS LTD., *Data Sheet* GI10, Tolworth, 1955.
[19] GRASEBY INSTRUMENTS LTD., *Data Sheet* GW3, Tolworth, 1955, see also *Flight*, 19 Aug. 1955.
[20] KLEINHOFER, B. A., Inst. of Navigation, U.C.L.A., 23 Jan. 1954.
[21] ANON., *American Aviation*, **18**, 11, 25 Oct. 1954, 98–106.
[22] CURTISS-WRIGHT, *Press Release*, 30 June 1955.
[23] SIMMONS, H. T., *American Aviation*, **19**, 14, 5 Dec. 1955, 32–34.
[24] VENN, J., *Jnl. Brit. Inter. Soc.*, **12**, 5, Sept. 1953, 213–25.
[25] BURGESS, E., *Aircraft*, **33**, 5, Feb. 1955, 28–33, 60.
[26] ABRAMSON, B. N., BRANDWEIN, D. S., MENES, H. C., *Jet Propulsion*, **24**, 5, Sept.–Oct. 1954, 291–6.
[27] BURGESS, E., loc. cit., 25.
[28] ANDERTON, D. A., *Aviation Week*, **59**, 9, 31 Aug. 1953, 24–26.
[29] ANON., *Jnl. American Rocket Soc.*, **23**, 6, Nov.–Dec. 1953, 378–9.
[30] RUMBLES, A. R., *Sperryscope*, **13**, 10, 1955, 4–7.
[31] GARDNER, G. W. H., *Chart. Mech. Eng.*, **2**, Jan. 1955, 5–22.
[32] ANON., *Aeronautics*, **31**, 5, Dec. 1954, 75.

CHAPTER V

GROUND-TO-AIR MISSILES

◎

OF ALL the classes of missiles it is in the defence interceptor type that perhaps the greatest development has taken place during the years since World War II, certainly the most rapid one. The advent of the atomic bomb created an urgency for the perfection of a more effective defence against attacking aircraft than could be given by manned fighters. One hundred per cent success of interception has to be aimed at if cities are to resist bombing attacks. Over the past years details have been released of a number of target defence missiles, and although more advanced designs of most of these will now be in production, these releases do give an indication of how missile defence is progressing from an experimental stage to one where guided missiles can be relied upon to defend a city or an industrial area from attack by conventional atomic bombers.

Before the more modern weapons are discussed it is of importance to trace the historical development of the ground-to-air missile. In all of the chapters concerning types of missiles, a large proportion of the historical sections will be devoted to German missiles because it is known that many of the present-day Soviet missiles have been developed directly from them. For example the WASSERFALL is in service with the Soviet armed forces while TAIFUN and RHEINTOCHTER have been further developed.[1] The SCHMETTERLING Hs. 117 design has also produced a modern weapon. Considerable detail will be given of some of these German designs because these have not been previously published in a permanent form.

During the concluding phases of World War II Germany made an attempt to counter the devastating bombing attacks of mounting Allied air supremacy by the production of unexpected new weapons, the ground-to-air interceptors which were propelled, in the main, by rocket motors, propulsion devices in which Germany undoubtedly led the field in those days.

A small missile, known as TAIFUN,[2] constructed by Electro-mechanishwerke, consisted of a long slim tube 75·6 in (190 cm) in length and 3·9 in (9·9 cm) in diameter, with a pointed nose and four small stabilizing fins. The average maximum height reached by the missile was in the neighbourhood of 50,000 ft (15,000 m), and the range was nearly 7·5 miles (12 km). A maximum velocity of 4,000 ft per sec (1,200 m/s) was attained, and the full starting weight was 110 lb (50 kg). This weight was divided between 43 lb (19 kg) structural weight, 22 lb (10 kg) of liquid propellants, and about 40 lb (18 kg) for the warhead. At the nose of the TAIFUN the warhead was situated together with its associated fuse, and following this was a cordite charge used to generate pressure for displacing the liquid propellants into the combustion chamber. A bursting disc separated the compartment containing the cordite from the head of the propellant tanks, and was designed to rupture at a pressure of 2·5 to 5 atmospheres. Concentric propellant tanks formed the next compartment, 15·9 lb (7·2 kg) of concentrated nitric acid (Salbei)* being housed in the central one and 5·73 lb (2·6 kg) of Visol, which was a mixture of butyl ether with analine, in the outer. Below the propellant tanks, at the extreme rear of the projectile, there was the combustion chamber and nozzle with an overall length of 27 in (68·5 cm) and a maximum diameter of 3·8 in (9·65 cm). The nozzle throat was 0·18 in (0·5 cm) in diameter and a 12-in (30·4 cm) expansion cone led to a mouth diameter of 3·5 in (8·9 cm). Four fins, each with an area of 24 sq in (155 sq cm), were attached to the tail in order to give arrow stability as this missile was unguided.

The burning of the cordite charge developed gases at a maximum pressure of about 50 atmospheres which displaced the propellants into the reaction chamber. To prevent spillage of the propellants during storage and transport, there were also bursting discs between the propellant tanks and the injectors at the head of the combustion chamber. When fired Visol passed immediately into the chamber, but it was not until the gases began to issue from the nozzle that a special valve operated and opened to admit Salbei. Spontaneous combustion then took place and the motor developed a thrust of 2,200 lb (1,000 kg) which gradually fell to 1,320 lb (600 kg) during the run of 3 sec. A specific impulse of 100 sec was obtained with a jet flow of 9·6 lb per sec (4·4 kg/s). Because the motor was only

*The Germans gave a code name to many propellants.

used once and the duration of power was so short, regenerative cooling was not required.

TAIFUN was, however, an unguided projectile and is of interest mainly because it represents one of the first rocket-propelled anti-aircraft weapons and this type of missile has been developed both in the East and the West. The modern American version is the Bendix LOKI which is powered by a Grand Central solid-propellant rocket. In Russia TAIFUN is used in the original liquid-propellant version for both ship-board and shore launchings.

Some of the larger type of rocket vehicles which are best catalogued between conventional aircraft and guided missiles can next be con-sidered. Two of this type were under development in Germany and were known as the ENZIAN and the NATTER. ENZIAN[3] was a ground-to-air pilotless aircraft which had a similar outline to the Me 163 target-defence interceptor fighter, for it was essentially a small air-craft with sharply swept-back wings. As in the Me 163, two ailerons were incorporated for control purposes, but at launching ENZIAN was mounted on a large inclined platform from which take-off at a high angle was assisted by means of solid-propellant boosters mounted in pairs at the wing roots.

Several versions of this weapon were being developed, and al-though these had been tested with different power units the missile had not found operational use by the end of World War II. E-1, E-2, and E-3 employed Walter units with turbo-driven propellant pumps for feeding the T-stoff and C-stoff which were used. E-4 and E-5, however, had bi-propellant motors designed by Konrad. Most of the available details relate to the E-4, which was designed to reach a height of 45,000 ft (13,400 m) and to have a range of some 25 miles (40 km). The overall length of this model was 380 in (9·65 m), and the maximum body diameter was 88 in (2·2 m). The wings, which had a span of 398 in (10 m), were swept back at an angle of 30 deg on the leading edge, their total area being 232 sq ft (21·5 sq m).

Included in the all-up weight at the time of take-off of 4,350 lb (1,970 kg) was 795 lb (360 kg) of assisted take-off units, 1,320 lb (599 kg) of propellants and a liquid-rocket unit which had a dry weight of 213 lb (97 kg). This unit developed a thrust of 4,400 lb (2,000 kg) which, however, decayed to 2,200 lb (1,000 kg) during the 70 sec run. Propellants used were Salbei and Visol (S.I. 181 sec) in the respective weights of 1,070 lb (485 kg) and 255 lb (116 kg). Compressed air was employed to displace propellants from the storage tanks into the combustion chamber. It was stored at a pressure of 200 atmospheres, but it had to pass through reducing valves before being applied to the tanks at a pressure of only 27 atmospheres. Burning took place in the combustion chamber at a pressure of about 20 atmospheres, and the total impulse generated amounted to 308,000 lb sec (139,700 kg sec). Assisted take-off was accomplished with four Schmidding 109–553 diglycol-dinitrate rockets, which were held in place by explosive bolts. As in other missiles the expansion nozzles were inclined at an angle to the general axis of the rocket so that the thrust line would pass through the centre of gravity of the missile, and apparently the setting of these boosters was quite critical if stability was to be ensured. Each of the rockets weighed 187 lb (85 kg) excluding their 22 lb (10 kg) of attachment gear. Moreover, they contained 88 lb (40 kg) of solid propellant and developed a total impulse of 15,435 lb sec (7,000 kg sec) with a specific consumption of 19·4 lb per lb hr, and a specific impulse of 182 sec. The length of each rocket was 93 in (2·36 m) and the maximum diameter was 6·6 in (16·7 cm), and burning for 4 sec they developed a thrust of 3,859 lb (1,750 kg). Under their influence the missile reached a velocity of about 820 ft per sec (250 m/sec).

ENZIAN E-5 also had a Konrad bi-propellant rocket unit which employed Salbei and Br-stoff (gasoline) in the respective total weights of 710 lb (322 kg) and 510 lb (231 kg). Spark ignition was used and the thrust developed was 5,500 lb (2,500 kg) decaying to 3,300 lb (1,500 kg) during the run of 56 sec. A specific impulse varying between 199 and 182 sec was obtained from this motor, and the total impulse amounted to 242,000 lb sec (110,000 kg sec). Propellant feed was again by compressed air, which was stored at a pressure of 200 atmospheres and was applied by reducing valves to the tanks so as to give an initial combustion chamber pressure of 34 atmospheres, decaying to 18 atmospheres.

NATTER was a somewhat similar but larger weapon. It differed from ENZIAN in that it was designed to carry a human pilot who could take over control after an almost vertical and automatically-controlled ascent. When interception had been completed provision was made for the pilot to descend to Earth by parachute. Construction was mainly of wood with short wooden wings. Produced by

Bachem with the official designation BP-20, it could reach a speed of just over 600 m.p.h. (960 km/hr) in level flight.

Assisted take-off was used in conjunction with a Walter bi-propellant rocket unit in order to propel the NATTER vertically, and indeed the rate of climb was so very great that a height of just over 37,000 ft (11,000 m) could be reached in 1 min. Because a human pilot was included it was necessary to restrict the acceleration to an amount which he could withstand. Having reached the required altitude, the pilot took over the controls and guided the missile towards the bomber formation. A nose cap, covering the several rocket discharge tubes, was then jettisoned and 24 rocket projectiles could be fired against the target. This armament consisted of 73 mm rockets, each of which weighed 5·7 lb (2·6 kg) and contained just under 1 lb of high explosive.

Specifications had also been issued by the German War Ministry for the production of a large anti-aircraft missile capable of attacking individual bombers and destroying them with a reasonable amount of success. The German High Command ordained that an operational accuracy of at least 50 per cent must be assured before the weapon could be accepted. Several research teams commenced to work on this project, and two main weapons were produced; but nevertheless, development along these lines had not been completed by the end of hostilities and the missiles themselves were not used operationally.

As an off-shoot from the A-series development of long-range rockets at Peenemünde, which ultimately produced the A-4, there

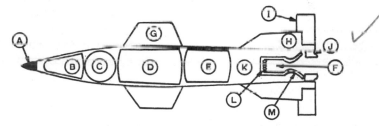

FIG. 5.1. *Diagram of the WASSERFALL, an early German ground-to-air missile which had been developed by Russia and also formed the aerodynamic shape for the HERMES missile of the General Electric Company. The letters indicate: A, proximity fuse; B, warhead; C, Nitrogen bottle; D, Salbei tank; E, Visol tank; F, rocket motor; G, stub wings; H, tail fin; I, control vanes; J, jet vanes; K, control department; L, propellant injectors; and M, coolant jacket to combustion chamber and nozzle.*

appeared the WASSERFALL.[4] This was a large projectile very similar in appearance to, though somewhat smaller than the well-known A-4 rocket. The general arrangement of the internal components of the missile is shown in the figure. At the nose was a radio proximity fuse which was designed to explode the 220 lb (100 kg) warhead when the WASSERFALL approached the target. After the warhead was the spherical pressure tank in which 154 lb (70 kg) of compressed nitrogen was stored under a pressure of 200 atmospheres, and used to displace the propellants from the tanks to the combustion chamber. Following on this was the oxidizer tank which contained 3,300 lb (1,500 kg) of Salbei, and then the tank for the 1,000 lb (454 kg) of Visol. At the extreme rear of the rocket was the combustion chamber of regenerative design, and cooled by the circulation of the nitric acid round the walls. Salbei flowed from an annulus at the nozzle mouth back around the nozzle and the combustion chamber to many small injector holes arranged in the injector plate at the head of the chamber. Visol, on the other hand, passed first to a reservoir at the head of the chamber from which it was injected through a large number of holes interspersed between those for the Salbei injection. The throat diameter was 7·6 in (19·3 cm) and the chamber pressure was 15 atmospheres. The resultant thrust was 17,600 lb (8,000 kg), the duration of power 41 sec, and the specific impulse 180 sec.

Four small stubby wings, each 24 in (61 cm) in span, and having a root and tip chord respectively of 84 in (213 cm) and 42 in (107 cm), were situated midway along the body, slightly larger fins at the extreme rear terminated in movable control surfaces which were operated by Siemens K-12 servomotors. Graphite vanes were also used as control surfaces by being inserted in the efflux stream. The overall length of the missile was 236 in (508 cm) and the maximum body diameter was 27·5 in (69·8 cm), launching was to be accomplished from a mobile launching cradle, and the missile was to travel vertically upwards for about 6 sec, after which time control would be taken over by the radio controller. It was anticipated that sonic velocity would be reached 20 sec after launching, and the projectile could be further accelerated to a maximum velocity in the region of 2,000 ft per sec (610 m/sec). The total height reached would be in the region of 33,000 ft (10,000 m) but the horizontal range would not exceed 20 miles (32 km). Although the first of this type of missile was tested as early as 1944, it is thought that less than fifty were actually fired, and development was by no means complete. Control for the WASSERFALL was a beam rider guidance system.

WASSERFALL production in Soviet hands[5] has since equipped missile launching sites to screen Moscow, Leningrad, and other defence areas.

Rheinmetal Borsig also produced a guided missile to these specifications. It was known as the RHEINTOCHTER[6] and there were two types, the R-1 and the R-3.

RHEINTOCHTER R-1 was a radio-controlled, two-stage rocket launched at an angle of about 70 deg against bomber formations. Take-off was assisted by a large booster rocket which comprised the first stage and which was spigotted on to the stern of the primary rocket. This missile was launched from a more complicated mobile launching ramp than the WASSERFALL. R-1 had a slant range of about 24 miles (38 km), a ceiling of about 20,000 ft (6,000 m), and a maximum velocity in the neighbourhood of twice that of sound.

The overall length was 226 in (574 cm), of which 142 in (361 cm) consisted of the primary rocket, and the remainder of the booster.

FIG. 5.2. *The RHEINTOCHTER R-1 anti-aircraft guided missile.*

The general lay-out is shown in the figure. At the nose of the primary rocket was the conical Kugelblitz proximity fuse, immediately after which was a compartment containing the servomotors needed to actuate the four small control fins which were mounted in this section. These wooden fins each had a span of 15·5 in (39·4 cm) and a root chord of 40 in (35·5 cm), and they had sections with rounded leading and flat trailing edges. In order to give control in elevation two of these surfaces were linked together, while the other two determined the direction of the flight. Against the elevators were markings on the aluminium casing which indicated a range of angular settings between plus or minus 10 deg from the axial positions. The next compartment contained gyroscopes, radio, batteries, and a vibrator unit for generating the high-tension supply needed for the anodes of the valves of the transmitter and the receiver. This compartment was secured by eighteen bolts to a steel motor cylinder which was 44·5 in (113 cm) in length and 20 in (51 cm) in diameter, with a dished end at the rear into which six nozzles were screwed. The thickness of the base plate was 1·25 in (3.17 cm) and the walls were also of the same thickness for a distance of about 4 in (10·2 cm) from the nozzle, after which their thickness became only 0·125 in (3·175 mm). At the nozzle end there was, moreover, a perforated base plate for the support of the 485 lb (220 kg) of diglycol propellant which gave the primary rocket a total impulse of 88,000 lb sec (40,000 kg sec). The nozzles were splayed outwards so that the hot gases would clear the booster unit during the initial stages of the flight, and each nozzle was 10·4 in (26·4 cm) long and had a throat and mouth diameter of 1·58 in (4·0 cm) and 3 in (7·62 cm) respectively. Constructed from a short machined steel throat section, which included a portion of expansion cone, the nozzles had an additional length of cone welded from sheet steel.

Secured by twenty-four bolts to the rear of the motor cylinder was a streamlined light alloy casing which served as a fin attachment and warhead compartment, into slots on which were fitted six wings. The splayed expansion nozzles of the motor protruded through slots in this section between the wings, and the 50 lb (22·6 kg) warhead was supported by six heavy steel internal guides.

The six wings were each 2 in thick at the roots, where the chord was 28 in (71 cm) but tapered to a thickness of ·5 in and a chord of 10 in (25·4 cm) at the tips. The rounded leading edge was swept back a distance of 40 in (102 cm) and the span was 104 in (264 cm). The trailing edges were flat and, except for wooden leading edges, construction was in the form of a laminated wooden core with aluminium facings, the whole being secured together by means of rivets which were finally filed flush with the surface of the wings. The total weight of the primary rocket was 2,200 lb (1,000 kg); it developed a thrust of approximately 35,300 lb (16,000 kg) for a period of 2·5 sec.

The booster section consisted mainly of a steel cylinder, 20 in (51 cm) in diameter and 51 in (129 cm) in length, which contained 530 lb (240 kg) of diglycol-dinitrate solid propellant. The dished base of the cylinder had welded on to it seven expansion nozzles, two of which were blocked at the throat, and inside the cylinder, at the nozzle end, was a perforated steel plate for the support of the grains of propellant. The nozzles were of welded steel construction. They had a total length of 10 in (25·4 cm), a throat diameter of 3·5 in (10·4 cm), a mouth diameter of 6·5 in (16·5 cm) and a divergent cone 7 in (17·8 cm) long. The burning time of the motor was only 0·6 sec and the thrust developed was 16,500 lb (7,480 kg). The specific propellant consumption was normal for this type of rocket, being 20 lb per lb hr.

The steel cylinder of the booster rocket unit was secured by eighteen bolts to a magnesium annulus, which in turn was connected to the primary rocket by four bolts. An aluminium fin attachment collar in halves was bolted around the main cylinder and included a steel launching guide and fin attachments consisting of slots into which four fins could be inserted and locked into position. The fins on this booster section were rather larger than those on the primary, each being 87 in (220 cm) in span with root and tip chords of 32·5 in (82·5 cm) and 12 in (30·4 cm) respectively. The leading edge was swept back at an angle of about 45 deg, and the section had a maximum thickness of 1 in (2·54 cm). V-shaped metal spars supported the fins and helped to give them rigidity. The total weight of the booster was 1,650 lb (748 kg) and the weight of the rocket cylinder with propellant amounted to 1,430 lb (650 kg).

The later model, known as RHEINTOCHTER R3, was designed to use a liquid-propellant primary rocket motor constructed by Konrad. The overall length of this missile was 187 in (475 cm) with a maximum body diameter of 21·25 in (54 cm). Including 739 lb (335 kg) of Salbei, and 194 lb (88 kg) of Visol, the total weight of the primary rocket was 1,185 lb (537 kg) and the regenerative motor developed a thrust which varied during the flight. Commencing at 4,800 lb (2,170 kg) it remained at that value for 5 sec, after which it was automatically reduced to 3,960 lb (1,800 kg) to remain constant for the remaining 38 sec of the run. The specific impulse obtained was 181 sec, and the total impulse 80,000 lb sec (36,300 kg sec). Propellant feed was by compressed air stored at a pressure of 250 atmospheres, which was sufficiently reduced by valves before being applied to the tanks so as to create a chamber pressure of 20 atmospheres. The length of the combustion chamber was 17·7 in (45·0 cm) and the nozzle throat had a diameter of 7 in (17·8 cm).

The booster charge gave a thrust of 31,000 lb (14,000 kg) for a period of 0·9 sec with a total impulse of 27,800 lb sec (12,600 kg sec). Diglycol-dinitrate was again used as propellant and 330 lb (150 kg) of it were carried. The total weight of the booster, two of which were used with each primary rocket, was 485 lb (220 kg). This missile has also been further developed by Soviet rocket experts.

It was intended that these large anti-aircraft missiles should be guided by the Rheinland system of radio and radar control.[7] This consisted of two radar detectors—one followed the missile while the other tracked the aircraft—and a control bunker which contained a Siemens computer. This latter recorded the signals from the radars, and the operator attempted alignment by manual control, during which process the resulting impulses caused signals to be sent through a transmitter at a frequency of 1,200 Mc/s to the receiver in the projectile. The equipment on the missile consisted of a receiver, from which the signals were sent through a matching unit to the servomechanism, which in turn operated the control surfaces. A transmitter was also provided to give a recognition signal and thus facilitate the following of the missile by radar.

By this radio control it was possible to guide the projectile on to the line of sight from the operator to the target aircraft; but in the case of radar jamming by 'window' or other means, it was intended that guiding should be made possible by means of flares attached to the fins or to the tail. If visual guiding were used the method would have been to sight on the flares by means of a telescope which was aligned by coupling with a radar reflector, and then to keep the cross-wires of the telescope, the target, and the missile in the same straight line. The projectile would ultimately have been detonated by a radio-actuated fuse, but as this may have been difficult to accomplish at supersonic speed, it was intended to develop a proximity fuse or a homing device.

Another anti-aircraft type of guided missile was constructed by Henschell and was called the SCHMETTERLING (Hs.117).[8] This missile was designed by Professor Wagner and there were several models under development at the close of hostilities, but although some were ready for quantity production, difficulty in the supply of booster units prevented the weapon from being used operationally. Launching was assisted by two solid-propellant rockets which were jettisoned after 4 sec of flight, by which time the main liquid-propellant unit was operating.

Radio signals from the ground, picked up and analysed by receivers situated in the nose behind the warhead, caused electro-magnetic servos to operate spoilers on the wings and tail surfaces in order to control the direction of flight. A flare was included in the tail to assist guidance when atmospheric conditions permitted.

The overall length of the missile was 157 in (4·0 m) and the fuselage was cylindrical in shape, being built up from three main sections. An asymmetrical nose housed the warhead and proximity fuse on the port side, and a wind-driven electrical generator on the other. The tail section was of sheet alloy with a casting at the extreme rear to support the tail and the rear of the rocket motor.

The wings and the tail unit were produced as castings from light alloy, the cantilever tail unit being made in two symmetrical sections, which were interchangeable. The whole structure of wings, tail plane, fins and fuselage was covered with a light-alloy skin.

With a chord at the roots of 26 in (66 cm) the mid-wings tapered to 12·5 in (31·7 cm) at the tips, and the leading edge was sharply swept back about 24 in (61 cm). The two spoilers, which operated in the place of ailerons, were each 13 in (33 cm) in length and were actuated by solenoids. The wing itself, as in the Hs.298 which will be described in the next chapter, was attached by a single tubular steel spar which passed through three of the ribs. The tail plane was 39 in (99 cm) in span and instead of the normal type of elevators it had electrically operated spoilers.

The operating ceiling of the SCHMETTERLING was about 35,000 ft (10,500 m), and it had an absolute ceiling of nearly 50,000 ft (15,000 m). Maximum speed was attained just after take-off when the booster units were operating, and this was almost Mach 0·90, but it soon fell to Mach 0·75, and in later models to Mach 0·80, although in some types the speed was even restricted to Mach 0·23. This limitation of the speed to a constant Mach number was accomplished by a Machmeter; whereby the propellant valves were regulated by ram pressure while an altimeter controlled the thrust. The horizontal range of the missile varied, the maximum being about 20 miles (32 km) with a 50 lb (22·7 kg) warhead, but a modification was being made to include a more destructive warhead weighing 88 lb (40 kg). Presumably this was because the guidance system could not be relied upon to bring the missile close enough to its target. Excluding the boosters, but including the main rocket motor, the structural weight of the SCHMETTERLING amounted to about 375 lb (170 kg). The total weight at take-off was nearly 1,000 lb (450 kg) but this figure varied with the different models.

One type of Hs.117 used a BMW 109–558 rocket motor, which weighed 350 lb (158 kg) full and 185 lb (84 kg) dry. The overall length of this unit was 107 in (271 cm) and the maximum diameter was 13·8 in (35·2 cm). The propellants used were 98 per cent nitric acid, and Tonka, which was 57 per cent oxide m-xylidine plus 43 per cent tri-ethylamine. The respective weights of these two propellants were 130 lb (59 kg) and 28 lb (12·7 kg). This propellant combination gave a specific impulse of 175 sec.

The nitric acid was housed in the rear propellant tank and, by circulation around the walls of the combustion chamber and nozzle, it was used as a coolant. To displace the propellants into the reaction chamber, compressed air, at a pressure of 205 atmospheres, was contained in a bottle constructed of two welded halves of pressed steel, situated at the front of the missile.

A chamber pressure of 20·5 atmospheres was obtained with a total impulse of 27,500 lb sec (12,500 kg sec). The thrust actually commenced at a value of 836 lb (380 kg) but decayed during the run of 60 sec to a final value of 132 lb (60 kg). At full thrust the duration could be only 35 sec.

For another model a 109–729 Walter rocket was employed. This utilized nitric acid and petrol and it had a full weight of 330 lb (150 kg) with a dry weight of 143 lb (65 kg). The propellants were divided as 150 lb (68 kg) of nitric acid and 68 lb (30 kg) of petrol.

They were displaced into the combustion chamber by means of compressed air stored at 184 atmospheres. The acid was again used for regenerative cooling of the motor.

For starting purposes in this unit furfuryl alcohol was used with squib ignition and the total impulse developed was 27,600 lb sec (12,500 kg sec). The chamber pressure was approximately 27·3 atmospheres and this resulted in a full thrust of 831 lb (377 kg). This value decayed to 132 lb (60 kg) during the thrust period of 60 sec.

On both of these units the motor was supported by thrust rods, by which it was attached to the rear propellant tank. This design enabled the rocket motor to be situated at the extreme rear of the missile, so that a fuselage step was not needed for the exhaustion of the propellants.

Manufactured by Schmidding, the 109–553 boosters were mounted one each above and below the fuselage of the main missile. Each was 94 in (239 cm) in length and 6·6 in (16·75 cm) in diameter and weighed 187 lb (85 kg). The 88 lb (40 kg) of diglycol propellant gave a total impulse of 15,400 lb sec (6,985 kg sec) and a thrust of 3,850 lb (1,750 kg) and was achieved with the propellants producing a specific impulse of 183 sec.

As mounted on the SCHMETTERLING, the boosters had nozzles which were inclined at an angle of 30 deg, so that their thrust line would pass through the centre of gravity of the missile. The boosters were jettisoned as soon as their charge was exhausted. In many of the early tests the missile rolled during flight.

Apart from German work one of the earliest missiles in this class was the Fairchild LARK.[9] This vehicle was first produced as a defence against *Kamikazi* planes, the project being started in 1945; but in the years following the war the Fairchild Company developed the semi-active homing guidance system until it was claimed as being one of the most advanced devised. The missile itself was 13 ft 11 in (4·24 m) in length and had a diameter of 18 in (45·7 cm). Four extruded aluminium wings arranged in a cruciform pattern had a tip to tip span of 6 ft 3 in (1·9 m), while a cruciform tail unit, rotated 45 deg from the planes of the wing surfaces, had a span of about 4 ft (1·2 m). The launching weight of the missile was 1,210 lb (550 kg). (*Fig.* 5.3.)

Take-off from a zero-length launching cradle was made with two solid-propellant booster rockets housed in a jettisonable box-fin

FIG. 5.3. *The Fairchild LARK missile is launched from the U.S.S. Norton Sound by solid propellant booster rockets. The missile was originally designed as a U.S. Navy project during the latter months of World War II as a defence against Japanese suicide planes and it is now used by all three branches of the Armed Services in their training and evaluation programmes.*
(Photo. Fairchild Engine & Airplane Corp.)

structure reminiscent of the RHEINTOCHTER booster. The launcher collapsed as the missile moved forward so that there could be no fouling of any part of the structure during the take-off. The main propulsion unit was a RMI liquid-propellant acid-aniline motor having two thrust cylinders. One of these was used for cruising at about Mach 0·9 while the other was a reserve standby for added power during manœuvres. Propellants were stored within plastic bags in the propellant tanks and were displaced to the combustion chamber by compressed air stored at 33 atmospheres pressure. The body was fabricated from aluminium alloy with a fibreglass nose section in which was housed the radar equipment. Some aerials were embedded in the fibreglass tail surfaces. The LARK has a range of about 10 miles (16 km) and is now used as a component test vehicle for developing the techniques of handling, launching and guidance.

Another early sea-to-air missile was LITTLE JOE which used forward cruciform control surfaces, a cruciform wing, and a solid-propellant rocket motor. This vehicle was officially designated KAN-2.

The Boeing Aircraft Corporation also started work in this field at an early date with their GAPA projects for rocket and ramjet vehicles. (*Fig.* 5.4.) The early GAPA rockets took several forms, one

FIG. 5.4. *The GAPA series of firings lead to the BOMARC. This test vehicle shows the wing plan form which is now a feature of the production missile.*

(Photo. Boeing Airplane Co.)

of which consisted of a 10 ft (3 m) missile using an Aerojet bi-propellant rocket and a solid-propellant booster. Over 100 GAPAS were
flown and served to develop the modern missile for the United States
Air Force. The production missile, of which some details have recently been released, is, however, a ramjet vehicle. Presumably it is
developed from the early GAPA ramjets one of which was some 26 ft
(8 m) in length—10 ft (3 m) without the booster—and had a
diameter of 12 in (30·4 cm). This missile was boosted by a solid-
propellant rocket and sustained flight with the ramjet was at a speed
of Mach 2. Cruciform fins were used for guidance.

The missile now in production is called the BOMARC (*Fig.* 5.5)
which is designed for long-range interception. It uses an integral
rocket unit by Aerojet for booster purposes, and then relies on two

FIG. 5.5. *A drawing of the BOMARC ground-to-air long-range interceptor
missile which is powered by two Marquardt ramjets and uses a rocket
boosted take-off.* (Photo. Boeing Airplane Co./U.S. Air Force)

Marquardt ramjets, mounted in pods beneath the wings in typical Boeing style, for maintaining speed in the supersonic region. The BOMARC is 66 ft (20 m) long, has a wing span of 36 ft (11 m), and was developed jointly by the Boeing Aircraft Company and the Michigan Air Research Council. It weighs about 8,500 lb (3,850 kg) and its top speed is about Mach 2·5, its ceiling is in the region of 80,000 ft (24,000 m) and it has a probable range of about 250 miles (400 km). Beam rider control is used with radar homing.

For the U.S. Navy, Convair produces the TERRIER missile, which employs solid-propellants for both the sustaining motor and the booster. This missile has a launching weight of 3,300 lb (1,500 kg), a ceiling of about 50,000 ft (15,000 m) and is radio controlled. Large numbers of this missile are being manufactured and it is intended to equip the United States Navy's first combatant guided-missile ships, the heavy cruisers *Boston* and *Canberra* both of which are being commissioned in 1956. The TERRIER has a speed of about Mach 2 and an effective range of nearly 20 miles (32 km). It is controlled by a beam rider system with target homing. Production began in 1951. The missile itself is about 15 ft (4·5 m) long and its diameter 12 in (30·4 cm). The solid-propellant rocket is made by Aerojet.

In recent trials TERRIER took off from the deck of a converted battleship, the USS *Mississippi* (*Fig.* 5.6) on a mission for destroying an attacking 'enemy' aircraft simulated by a target drone. (*Fig.* 5.7.) It is claimed that this missile can find and destroy its target under any conditions of visibility and weather. It has been adopted by the Marine Corps as the first anti-aircraft missile for use in amphibious operations.

TERRIER was developed for the Navy Bureau of Ordnance by Convair Division of the General Dynamics Corporation under the technical direction of Johns Hopkins University Applied Physics Laboratory. It is now produced at the Pomona, California, plant of Convair.[10]

A ship-to-air missile like the TERRIER may cost over £6,000 to manufacture. But this is by no means the whole of the cost of such a defensive system. When installed in a battleship the ship-board equipment, radar, computer, launching devices, pre-flight checking equipment, etc., may amount to nearly £2 million.[11]

The NIKE system is, however, the first complete interceptor system on which details have been released by security. Sponsored by the

FIG. 5.6. *A Convair TERRIER is shown immediately after take-off under rocket boost from the deck of the converted battleship U.S.S. Mississippi. This missile is to be used from the guided missile ships U.S.S. Boston and U.S.S. Canberra and also by the Marines for amphibious operations.*

(Photo. Convair/United States Navy)

U.S. Army, NIKE batteries are being installed around certain vital defence areas, the first being at Washington DC, while more than 100 batteries will be spread throughout the United States to cover twelve other defence areas. All sites are expected to be completed by 1956 and will give complete air cover to those vital localities. Against normal aircraft spectacular results are obtained to judge from some tests carried out at White Sands. A B-17, flying at 30,000 ft (9,000 m) and taking evasive action, was intercepted and destroyed by a NIKE missile. The NIKE missile has also successfully intercepted a MATADOR missile in recent tests at White Sands.

NIKE has been under development for some time. Originally it had a clustered booster of four solid-propellant rockets with large fins. The production model, however, uses instead a single small-finned booster, while the missile itself seems shorter than the earlier version. This would give more rapid guidance response. In point of fact, the

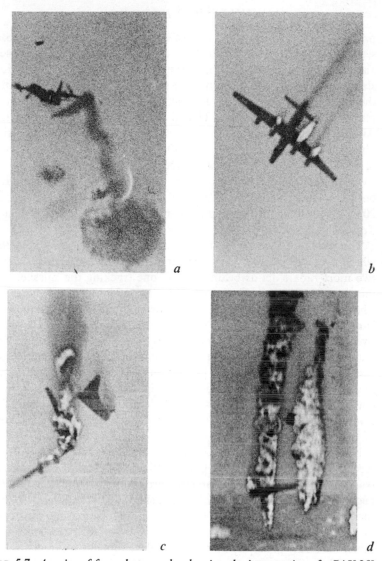

Fig. 5.7. *A series of four photographs showing the interception of a P4Y-2K target drone by the surface-to-air guided missile, the Convair TERRIER.* (a) *The trail of gases from the rocket motor shows how the TERRIER closed in to explode its warhead close to the target.* (b) *Just after the explosion fire bursts from one of the engines of the drone and quickly* (c) *the large four-engined bomber breaks up.* (d) *The flaming parts of the target aircraft plunge toward the Atlantic Ocean.*

(Photos. Convair Division of General Dynamics Corp.)

production missile has three sets of cruciform fins in addition to a set on the booster; the forward set of fins is for steering purposes and each fin moves as a whole about an axis, the rear set acts for stability. The reason for the middle set of tiny fins is not clear and the released statements give no indication of their purpose. They may be beam sensing devices. The missile is produced by the Douglas Aircraft Company with a control system from Western Electric. NIKE has a slant range of 25 miles (40 km) and a ceiling in the region of 70,000 ft (21,000 m). It is a supersonic missile powered by an Aerojet acid-aniline rocket motor and using a solid-propellant booster. The overall length with this booster amounts to about 20 ft (6 m) and the maximum diameter of the missile is 12 in (30·4 cm). Top speed is about Mach 2.

The guidance system for the NIKE consists of a radar detector which fires the missile when the target comes within range, while two more radars act as beam control, one tracking the missile and the other the target. Semi-active homing is used for terminal guidance. The control point is located between one and four miles from the two launching sites with which it is associated. The sites normally have two launching aprons, but in an emergency, provision is made for increasing these to six. The NIKEs can be static tested at the launching sites and are then loaded with propellants and stored in underground magazines, each of which holds about eighteen missiles. This storage ready for launching is a necessity with defence missiles, and calls for suitable propellant combinations. Nitric acid appears to be the best of the oxidizers for this purpose.

Named after the goddess of victory of Greek Mythology, NIKE resulted from eight years of guided missile research.[12] An integral part of the Army's guided missile programme, the NIKE project began in 1945 when Army Ordnance asked Bell Telephone Laboratories to undertake a study of the problems involved in the construction of a new anti-aircraft system. As a result of their recommendations, the Army promptly authorized a development contract so that the guided missile system could be brought to a reality.

Initial firing tests of NIKE missiles started in the Autumn of 1946, and throughout the intervening years the NIKE missile and its associated equipment progressed from one development stage to another. During early tests, 150,000 items of data were obtained from each test vehicle flight. These were processed through a data analyser. The missile was first fired without a warhead and it was observed by means of a wide-angle camera. Used also without a warhead against the target drone, homing to the drone was recorded by automatic high-speed and long-range cameras carried within the target. Finally, NIKE was ready for mass production.

This new addition to the United States arsenal of defence was developed by a combined service/industrial team composed of engineers of the Army Ordnance Corps, Western Electric Company, Bell Telephone Laboratories and Douglas Aircraft Company. The mass production of the control equipment is now largely in the hands of the Western Electric Company, while the missile and the component parts of the NIKE system are being produced by the Douglas Aircraft Company, Western Electric and several hundred suppliers and sub-contractors in over twenty states.

The NIKE system essentially consists of two parts; first, the expendable missile, second, the elaborate and highly complex control system requiring approximately 1,500,000 individual parts.

The NIKE system is claimed as providing a far greater degree of anti-aircraft protection than was previously possible with the more limited ranges and altitudes of conventional anti-aircraft devices.

Anti-aircraft defence by NIKE utilizes constructed emplacements. The missiles are stored in underground magazines[13] from which they are moved horizontally on a special trolley. An elevator carries them through a slit in the concrete bunker to the surface and hydraulic power raises them into the critical firing position. Two missile launchers have one underground magazine and there are two magazines to each launching base. The launching site itself is T-shaped with two missile launchers on the upright and the assembly, test and propellant-loading sections on the top bar of the T. At a distance of about one to four miles from the launching position is the control site which includes the tracking and identification radars. Loud hydraulic power units are used to raise the missile from the loading position to the firing position. (*Fig.* 5.8.)

It is claimed that the NIKE can outmanœuvre bombers, fighters or transport planes, and it can operate regardless of weather conditions and visibility. Moreover the system is mobile. All units of it other than the launching racks are housed in specially designed all-weather van-type trailers. If necessary, the system can be transported by air.

NIKE is fired from its launcher by a remotely-controlled missile launching mechanism, and in order to provide for maximum safety, the warhead is constructed so that it will explode only during flight.

The NIKE battery receives early warning from the air-warning net that hostile aircraft are approaching the area defended by it. The target is picked up and tracked automatically by the radar. At this stage the NIKE missiles are readied in a vertical position on their launching racks. A continuous record of the target's position is

FIG. 5.8. *The Nike I surface-to-air guided missile with booster attached is shown in the elevated launching position ready for a test firing at White Sands Proving Ground, New Mexico.* (Photo. U.S. Air Force)

transmitted to the controller, and at the same time the missile's control mechanisms, stabilization and navigational equipment are checked, and certain safety mechanisms are disengaged—the missile is armed. As the target crosses the distant and invisible line, which brings it into missile range, the NIKE is fired. Within seconds after launching the missile exceeds Mach 1 and travels at supersonic speed for the rest of its journey, riding smoothly on the power of its integral rocket engine.

Development of the NIKE really started in January 1944 when

the Anti-Aircraft Artillery Board submitted military requirements for a controlled anti-aircraft rocket projectile and recommended that a development programme using these military characteristics as a basis should begin. This was indeed one of the first official recognitions of the important point that a new type of weapon was essential to afford protection from the speedy and manœuvrable high-flying aircraft then in production or planned. It was concluded that merely matching speed with speed was insufficient because the initiative would remain with the aircraft. The new weapon must be able to manœuvre throughout its flight.

In 1945 the Army Ordnance Corps, which had the design, developments, and procurement responsibilities for all the missiles of the United States Army, asked Bell Telephone Laboratories to undertake a theoretical study of the problems involved in constructing a new anti-aircraft system. Five months later the recommendations of the Laboratories were submitted to the Army—a supersonic surface-to-air guided weapon system which relied upon simplicity in the missile itself.

A development contract resulted and Bell Laboratory Engineers started the task of bringing to reality the system their study had envisioned. The Douglas Aircraft Company became a full partner in the enterprise and was assigned responsiblity for about half the development effort, including the design of the missile and the launching equipment.

A period of nearly five years was required to solve the new and complex technical problems proposed by the NIKE system. During this time test firings to improve launcher and booster designs were made at the White Sands Proving Grounds in New Mexico. In the meantime, development of the guidance equipment proceeded at the Bell Telephone Laboratories.

The first test firings of the NIKE without guidance control took place in the autumn of 1946, and their immediate success confirmed some of the predictions made in the 1945 study.

Army Ordnance promptly placed production contracts with Western Electric, whose plants in several states were producing and furnishing important elements of the NIKE system. It is now estimated that well over 1,000 companies are contributing to the project.

A new version of the NIKE is planned to have a range of 50 miles (80 km) and a speed of at least Mach 3. NIKE can now be fitted with an atomic warhead[14] which is lethal to aircraft within 1,300 ft (400 m) of the explosion point. The present NIKE missile costs just over £7,000 without its warhead.[15]

Other missiles of this class being developed in the United States include the Raytheon HAWK, the Bendix TRITON, and the Bell SHRIKE. France is reported to have a surface-to-air missile developed from the Matra 0-4, while in Switzerland the Oerlikon Company has developed a surface-to-air missile (*Fig.* 5.9) which uses a bi-propellant rocket unit and a beam rider system of control. The length of the rocket is just under 20 ft (6 m) and its maximum diameter 1·25 ft (0·38 m). Its launching weight is 770 lb (350 kg) and it can reach a

FIG. 5.9. *This photograph shows the OERLIKON guided missile mounted on a twin launching device. These missiles do not use a boosted take-off.*

(Photo. Oerlikon Buhrle & Co.)

speed of 2,500 ft per sec (760 m/sec). The ceiling is reported to be over 60,000 ft (18,000 m) with a 44 lb (20 kg) warhead and the range 12·5 miles (20 km). The fuselage is constructed of plastic laminated wound metals. The rocket motor employs a nitric acid and kerosene propellant combination, and uses a special tri-ethylamine and xyladine fluid for ignition purposes. Nitrogen gas pressure is used to displace the propellants into the combustion chamber, the nitrogen being stored at 300 atmospheres. The rocket motor gives a thrust of 2,200 lb (1,000 kg) and the duration of burning is about 30 sec. The beam guidance uses a coarse beam of 20 deg included angle which gathers the missile after launching, thus bringing it into a tight 3 deg beam which directs the missile to its target.

There is a tremendous scarcity of information concerning British guided missile work. However, it was claimed in 1952[16] that 'guided weapons had been developed which can travel at well over 2,000 m.p.h. (3,200 km/hr) and can rise to heights far greater than any bomber is likely to reach for many years to come'. Basic research was undertaken by official experimental establishments and the results were then made available to selected firms who were entrusted with the task of developing specific rocket weapons to fulfil the various operational roles.

A year later another short statement[17] from the Ministry of Supply confirmed that the development of the rocket missiles took place initially in Britain at the experimental establishment of the Ministry of Supply and by industrial firms. Preliminary firing tests took place in Britain (*Fig.* 5.10) and success led to the missile being sent to Australia where full-scale trials, even with explosive warheads, could be carried out on the range at Woomera. Any modifications demanded by the results of these trials could then be made at the workshops close to the Australian range.

It was stated that one of the serious problems encountered was that connected with booster separation, but it was claimed this had been overcome. It was anticipated that new methods developed for moulding large plastic structures would enable the guided missile in the near future to use light plastics instead of metals. The results would not only be a reduction in weight without loss of strength but also a reduction in cost, which is, indeed, a matter of great importance when hundreds if not thousands of missiles have to be available for the defence of even a small island like Great Britain.

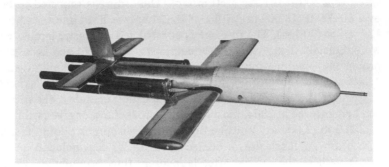

(a) *An early British surface-to-air missile was the Fairey STOOGE which was radio controlled and after being launched from a ramp by four cordite rockets which were jettisoned, continued its flight under the thrust of four more cordite rockets mounted within the missile itself. The Fairey Aviation Company are now producing an air-to-air missile known as the FIREFLASH.*

(Photo. Fairey Aviation Co. Ltd.)

(b) *Larger surface-to-air missiles are now under development in Britain and a number of test vehicles have been fired. This photograph shows a guided rocket with a tandem booster being fired at the Ministry of Supply Trial Establishment at Aberporth, Wales.* (Photo. Crown Copyright Reserved)

FIG. 5.10

It was also reported in 1955 that a surface-to-air guided weapon is being developed for naval use at sea. It was claimed in a White Paper[18] that good progress has been made in development of shipborne guided weapons. An experimental guided-weapon ship HMS *Girdleness*—originally a landing craft maintenance ship—has been converted for use in trials scheduled for 1956.

It is assumed that the ship-to-air anti-aircraft weapon is being made by Armstrong Whitworths and is a development of the test vehicle which was shown at the Farnborough Show in 1953. This test vehicle used wrap-around boosters. The sparse details which have been issued on Britain's efforts in the surface-to-air field have all been concerning rocket test vehicles and none of the weapons which are now in production has been described.

The ship-to-air weapon is reported to use a guidance system developed by the Sperry Gyroscope Company, while the rocket motor is produced by Armstrong Siddeley. Accordingly it may be that this weapon will use liquid oxygen as an oxidant.

The English Electric Company are reported to be producing a surface-to-air Mach 3 missile and this is believed to be in production and to use a Napier rocket unit together with a control system developed by another company in the group, Marconi. It is reported that this anti-aircraft weapon has a ceiling of 60,000 ft (18,000 m).

At a press conference at Farnborough on 20th February 1956 it was revealed that the first British guided weapon to shoot down a conventional aircraft was launched successfully on 7th April 1954. Fired from Aberporth rocket range the missile intercepted a Firefly which was radio guided to fly at 10,000 ft (3,000 m) at a range of 4·5 miles (7·2 km). This missile is now understood to be in production.

For training of personnel in the handling of surface-to-air missile systems it has been necessary to develop a number of missiles which are known as drones. They differ from operational missiles in that they are usually multi-shot devices and accordingly have to employ some kind of recovery device, usually a parachute.

Most target drones are winged and rely upon pulse-jets or short life turbo-jets for propulsion. Typical drones are represented by the British JINDIVIK (*Fig.* 8.1), the Ryan FIREBEE (*Fig.* 7.6) and the French ARS. 5501.

Surface-to-air weapons are being developed very rapidly especially in the United States and the Soviet Union. So much so that it will certainly be disappointing to the advocates of conventional bombers when they find that at the time the British V-bombers enter service with the Royal Air Force potential enemies have surface-to-air weapons which can achieve interception at distances of 50 miles from a target. The V-bombers will be unable to deliver their thermonuclear weapons.

Developments in guided missiles are quite likely to bring this about, and the answer, as will be shown in the next chapters, is first to produce air-to-ground weapons which can be launched beyond the range of surface-launched anti-aircraft missiles, then to produce strategic missiles to replace the bombers.

In view of these facts it has been suggested that the development of several different V-bombers by Britain is a waste of technical manpower and of money which could be far better spent in developing advanced air-to-surface and surface-to-surface missiles.

TABLE 5.1   *Ground-to-Air Missiles*

Name	Wasserfall	Lark	Bomarc	Terrier	Oerlikon	Nike
Manufacturer	Peene-münde	Fairchild	Boeing	Convair	Oerlikon	Douglas
Propulsion	LP.R	LP.R	Ramjet	SP.R	LP.R	LP.R
Booster	none	2 × SP.R	LP.R	SP.R	none	SP.R
Length, ft	20	14	66	15	20	20
Length, m.	6·1	4·3	20	4·6	6·1	6·1
Max. diam., in.	27·5	18	—	12	15	12
Max. diam., cm	70	45·5	—	30·4	38	30·4
Control system	Radio	Radio	Beam rider and homing	Beam rider and homing	Beam rider and homing	Beam rider and homing
Speed	Mach 2	Mach 2	Mach 2·5	Mach 3	Mach 2·5	Mach 3
Ceiling, ft	33,000	?	80,000	50,000	60,000	70,000
Ceiling, m	10,000	?	24,000	15,000	18,000	21,000
Range, miles	20	10	250	25	12·5	25
Range, km	32	16	400	40	20	40
Launching, lb,	7,800	1,210	8,500	3,360	770	1,000
Weight, kg	3,500	550	3,900	1,530	350	450
Status	Production	Production	Development	Production	Production	Production
Country	Germany and U.S.S.R.	U.S.A.	U.S.A.	U.S.A.	Switzerland	U.S.A.

Code: SP.R Solid-propellant rocket,   LP.R Liquid-propellant rocket

REFERENCES

[1] SMITH, J. F., *Inter Avia*, **10**, 5, May 1955, 300–9.
[2] BURGESS, E., *The Engineer*, **184**, 17 and 24 Oct. 1947, 356–8, 381–3.
[3] BURGESS, E., *The Engineer*, **184**, 24 Oct. 1947, 381–3.
[4] BURGESS, E., loc. cit., 3.
[5] SUTTON, G. P., *Jnl. American Rock. Soc.*, **23**, 3, May–June 1953, 186–9.
[6] BURGESS, E., *The Engineer*, **184**, 31 Oct. 1947, 407–9.
[7] MULLER, F., *Leitfaden der Fernlenkung*, Deutsche Radar Verlag., 1955, Ch. III.
[8] BURGESS, E., *The Engineer*, **184**, 10 Oct. 1947, 332–3.
[9] ANDERTON, D., *Aviation Week*, **52**, 21, 22 May 1950.
[10] CONVAIR, *Press Release*, 19 July 1955.
[11] *Financial Times*, 27 Jan. 1956, p. 1.
[12] U.S. ARMY, *Press Release*, 17 Dec. 1953, 17 Feb. 1954.
[13] ANON., *Inter Avia*, **10**, 5, May 1955, 316–17.
[14] ANON., loc. cit., 13.
[15] *Financial Times*, loc. cit., 11.
[16] MINISTRY OF SUPPLY, *Press Release*, 7, 26 July 1952.
[17] MINISTRY OF SUPPLY, *Press Release*, 6, 22 Aug. 1953, see also *Flight*, 28 Aug. 1953, p. 242.
[18] *British White Paper*, 17 Feb. 1955.

CHAPTER VI

AIR-LAUNCHED MISSILES

◎

A IR-LAUNCHED missiles comprise two main categories of guided weapons namely the air-to-air and air-to-surface missiles.

The first air-to-air missiles were simply unguided solid-propellant rockets,[1] which were launched from mountings under the wings of the aircraft or from pods attached to the wings or to the fuselage. However, during the concluding phases of World War II Germany introduced a number of airborne guided weapons which could be used against attacking aircraft.

One of these missiles was the Hs.298 which was designed early in 1944.[2] Mass production was planned for 1945 but development and testing had not been completed by the end of the war. This missile was intended for use with a solid-propellant rocket unit and was launched from fighter aircraft against bomber formations. It was released at a range of about one mile and was controlled by radio signals from the parent aircraft. In reality the missile was just a midget aircraft with small swept back wings. Construction was principally of sheet metal and a step was included in the fuselage design so that the rocket exhaust would clear the tail surfaces. The fuselage was quite deep, for in the upper half was housed the radio and control equipment, while the space beneath had to be sufficient for the rocket unit. The depth of the fuselage was thus 16 in (40·5 cm) with a maximum width of 8 in (20·3 cm). The proximity fuse and the warhead projected at the nose, while below them another projection housed a wind-driven generator and terminated in the airscrew for that generator.

The overall length of the Hs.298 was 79 in (200·6 cm) and the wing span was 50 in (127 cm). The mid-wings had not only a pronounced sweep back but also tapered from a root chord of 20 in (50·8 cm) to one of 9·25 in (23·5 cm) at the rounded tips. They were 2·25 in (5·72 cm) thick at the roots and were mounted on a single tubular main spar. Spoilers, each 6·375 in (16·2 cm) in length, gave lateral control in place of ailerons, and were operated by electromagnetic controls situated between the surfaces of the wings. The rectangular tail plane had an area of 200 sq in (12,090 sq cm) and a span of 21 in (53·3 cm), and on it were mounted two more spoilers to act in place of elevators. Attached to the tips of the tail plane were twin fins, but these had no movable control surfaces. In flight the Hs.298 attained a Mach number 0·7 to 0·8, and its all-up weight was in the neighbourhood of 200 lb (91 kg).

A specially designed solid-propellant unit in which the thrust was made to vary in flight was employed in this missile. Rapid acceleration was ensured at the moment of leaving the parent aircraft by a high thrust, but this was followed by a much longer period of power during which the thrust was at a reduced value. The system employed was for the propellant to be moulded in the form of a hollow cylinder. The surface of the hole down the centre of the cylinder was coated with a mixture of potassium silicate, asbestos and graphite, and the hole was then filled with the fast-burning propellant. Immediately after the ignition of the charge, combustion thus proceeded rapidly, producing a thrust of 330 lb (150 kg) for a period of about 5 sec. Restricted burning then followed, in which the thrust became 110 lb (50 kg) and remained at this value for a further 20 sec. On the average the rate of burning was 2·8 lb (1·27 kg) per second and the chamber pressure was approximately 120 atmospheres.

This motor was the 109–543 unit and it was designed by Henschell and constructed by Schmidding. It was 7 in (17·8 cm) in outside diameter and about 32 in (81 cm) in length, and included 70 lb (51·7 kg) of propellant. The nozzle was inclined at an angle as in many other German solid propellant rocket motors so that the thrust line would again pass through the centre of gravity of the missile. This system is also used quite extensively in a number of modern British missiles where wrap-around boosters are employed.

The X4[3] was also intended to be fired from fighter aircraft. It was remotely controlled from the parent aircraft by impulses transmitted along two insulated wires each of which was 0·008 in (0·02 cm) in diameter and 18,000 ft (5,500 m) in length. Two spools mounted on two of the four cruciform wings of the missile were used to contain the wires. The bobbins on which the wires were wound were housed in sheet steel containers 19 in (48·2 cm) long and 3 in (7·6 cm) in maximum diameter. At the front of these bobbin containers were stream-lined aluminium fairings, supported by a central rod and held in place by small plastic screw caps. To the other two wing tips flares were fitted in order that the position of the missile could be seen by the pilot of the fighter aircraft, who would thus be able to obtain manual guidance by means of a joystick type of control lever.

In flight the missile was caused to rotate at about sixty revolutions per minute by tabs attached to the trailing edge of the wings, and the controlling forces in direction and elevation had thus to be applied by causing spoilers on the cruciform tail unit to be operated so as to coincide with the period of roll. Control was indeed effected by vibrating the spoiler combs electro-magnetically at a frequency of about five times a second. The electrical impulses from the controller in the parent aircraft varied the duration of stay of the combs at each limit of their travel. Thus, when control had not to be applied, the spoilers remained for an equal length of time on each side of their axes, whereas for control purposes, the electro-magnets caused the spoilers to remain longer at one limit of travel than the other. This type of control was found to be effective even up to a Mach number of 0·9, while some measure of control existed at supersonic speeds, although under such conditions the spoiler controls of the Hs.117 or the Hs.298 were found to be more suitable.[4]

Released from the parent aircraft when it was flying several hundreds of miles per hour at an altitude of 20,000 ft (6,000 m), the missile was accelerated to a velocity of about 550 m.p.h. (880 km/hr) by the liquid-propellant rocket propulsion unit, which could, moreover, give an average rate of climb of 300 ft (91 m) per sec if needed. An almost tubular cast aluminium centre section housed the propellant tanks and propellant feed pressure tanks of the missile. Riveted to it were aluminium supports to which the four laminated wooden wings were bolted. The nose of the rocket missile consisted of a 55 lb (25 kg) warhead which was 18 in (45·7 cm) long, and a proximity or acoustic fuse. The warhead case of machined steel, 0·4 in (1 cm) in thickness, held 44 lb (20 kg) of high explosive and was bolted to the centre section. A sheet aluminium fairing attached the slender proximity fuse to the case of the warhead, and electrical connexions between the fuse and missile proper were made by wires which passed inside the warhead to an aluminium 8-pin plug, which was connected to a socket attached to the propellant tank compartment. Aft of the centre section was a riveted sheet-aluminium tail section, which enclosed the rocket motor, gyroscopes and electrical storage battery, and on which were mounted the four tail fins with the comb spoilers and their associated electro-magnets. An end-piece of pressed steel held the tail section securely in position by being screwed to a threaded collar which was welded to the outside of the nozzle. Also in this section was a 7-pin socket for connecting the missile electrically to the parent aircraft when X4 was in its launching carriage, which was a normal 250 lb (114 kg) bomb carriage. The total weight of X4 was 132 lb (60 kg) with propellants, and the overall length was 80 in (203 cm).

Propulsive power was obtained from a bi-propellant rocket motor, the BMW 109–548[5] which employed Salbei (SV-stoff) and Tonka (R-stoff). The propellant tanks and feed arrangements for this unit were rather unusual in that helical propellant tanks with flexible tank travellers were used. The propellant feed pressure tanks were arranged in tandem. Compressed air for the Salbei feed was stored in the forward cylindrical tank which was constructed of steel and had a diameter of 3 in (7·6 cm) and a length of approximately 11 in (28 cm). On the other hand, the pressure tank for the Tonka tapered from a maximum diameter of 3 in (7·6 cm) to one of 1·75 in (4·45 cm) at the extreme rear. It was situated aft of the Salbei tank and contained air at a pressure of 120 atmospheres.

Surrounding these two air bottles was a closely-wound helical coil of light alloy tubing which served as the Tonka fuel tank. The diameter of the tubing was 0·8 in (2 cm). The tank held 3·96 lb (1·8 kg) of fuel when fully loaded. Surrounding this coil was a second closely-wound helical tank of 1·2 in (3 cm) diameter light alloy tubing which contained 14·8 lb (6·7 kg) of nitric acid oxidizer. The whole of this tankage fitted neatly into the centre section of the X4 while supports, welded to the centre pressure tanks, held the unit in place by means of bolts through the base plate of the centre-section and the forward suspension spider.

From the head of the SV-stoff pressure tank, two air-pressure feed pipes passed to two separate electrically-operated valves which controlled the passage of the air to the dry side of each tank traveller. From these valves, steel pipes, 0·24 in (0·6 cm) in diameter, passed to the forward end of the helical tank.

The combustion chamber was mounted on three steel thrust rods, so that the exhaust nozzle projected at the rear of the missile. The motor was of the regenerative type in which Salbei circulated around the walls of the nozzle and the combustion chamber prior to injection from the head of the chamber. Construction was from machined steel with the head and multiple hole, impinging-type, injectors welded on. The chamber itself was 7 in (17·8 cm) long with an outside diameter of 3 in (7·6 cm), and the short expansion nozzle had a throat diameter of 0·56 in (1·43 cm), a mouth diameter of 1·75 in (4·45 cm), and an expansion cone of 1·5 in (3·8 cm) in length. The inner lining of the motor was welded to the outer jacket at the nozzle mouth, and also welded on to the outside of the nozzle was the threaded collar previously mentioned as being required for locking the tail section into position. A thrust of 242 lb (110 kg) was developed when the motor commenced to operate, but owing to the absence of pressure-reducing and regulating arrangements, this value gradually fell to zero during the run of between 17 and 20 sec. The initial combustion chamber pressure was 27 atmospheres, the specific impulse 154 sec, the specific propellant consumption 23 lb per lb hr, and the total impulse was 4,120 lb sec (1,870 kg sec).

The first model of X4 was constructed in April 1944, but this weapon was never used operationally. Due to the difficulties in the storage and handling of the nitric acid oxidizer and to control and stability problems which resulted from the decay in thrust during the flight, attempts were being made to develop a solid-propellant rocket unit for use in this missile. This had the designation 109–603 and in some experiments it gave a thrust of 330 lb (150 kg) for a period of 8 sec, but development and testing had not been completed by the end of hostilities.

Essentially the air-to-air missile is an aerial torpedo which is guided by the mother plane and also nowadays incorporates some kind of a homing device. Unless it is wire controlled, however, enemy interference may be used to prevent it from reaching its target. Quite a number of modern missiles are heat seekers, that is they home on infra-red radiation emanating from the target. These modern air-to-air missiles have a range of up to 7 miles (10 km), and are replacing the unguided rockets with which aircraft were formerly armed. In the case of the unguided rocket the method of attack is to use a large number fired in salvoes or in ripples. With the guided missile, however, one missile should be able to destroy one enemy aircraft. Such reliability has not yet been achieved but that is the ultimate goal. Perhaps the first missile of this type to be developed by a nation other than Germany was the Ryan FIREBIRD which was designed in 1946, and was used by the United States Air Force. An early version was fired by a solid-propellant booster rocket and then continued with four sustaining rockets which were triggered by Mach switches.

The FIREBIRD[6] was the product of a two-year experimental programme by the Ryan Aeronautical Company. It had a length of 10 ft (3 m) with a maximum diameter of 6 in (15·2 cm). A bi-propellant rocket unit was employed to give a sustaining thrust while a solid-propellant booster was used at take-off. The aerodynamic wing surfaces were in the form of a cruciform arrangement and had a 3 ft (91 cm) span; tail planes, also cruciform in arrangement and of similar span, gave manœuvrability. The FIREBIRD was guided by a radar navigational system and was aimed by radar at the time of launching from the mother aircraft. It homed on its objective and used a proximity fuse to give detonation at the minimum distance from the target. A destructive mechanism was incorporated so that the missile would destroy itself if it missed the target. Without the booster the missile itself was 7·5 ft (2·3 m) in length and weighed about 600 lb (472 kg). An active homing system was used to close in upon the target.

Another early American project was called HOT SPOT which was started in 1947. The idea was to produce a light and compact missile so that multiple units could be carried by fighter type aircraft. The outcome of this project was the rocket-powered radio-guided SPARROW. (*Fig.* 6.1.)

The SPARROW which was developed by the Sperry Gyroscope Company in co-operation with the Douglas Aircraft Company uses a solid-propellant rocket motor. Its overall weight is about 500 lb (220 kg) and the missile is about 8 ft long (2·4 m) with a diameter of 6 in (15·2 cm). Cruciform wings having a span of 2·25 ft (·685 m) are used and it is thought that the top speed is in the region of three times that of sound. The system of guidance is to use a beam rider and the missile also has a semi-active homing system for finally closing in to the target. Some test vehicles were fired from the ground using a large solid-propellant booster rocket. The range of this missile is probably of the order of 5 miles.

FIG. 6.1. *Four Sperry SPARROW air-to-air guided missiles are shown in the racks of a naval twin jet night fighter, the Douglas F3D Skynight.*
(Photo. United States Navy)

Present-day conception of a missile defensive system envisages first interception by long-range ramjet missiles such as the Boeing BOMARC operating at ranges of up to 200 miles (320 km) from the target area. Within 50 to 100 miles (80 to 160 km) interceptor fighters will engage the enemy using air-to-air missiles. Finally the inner ring of ground-to-air missiles of the Douglas NIKE type would destroy any bombers which may penetrate to within 25 miles (40 km) of the target. Consequently at the end of World War II first priority in most defence systems was given to the production of those air-to-air weapons which were needed to strengthen the existing forces of fighter aircraft which could be used for interception, and soon there was production of the FIREBIRD, the SPARROW, and unnamed British and Soviet missiles. It was claimed in a Ministry of Supply statement[7] that British air-to-air missiles which could be launched from fighter aircraft had reached an advanced stage in development. It was claimed too that these missiles would enable the fighters to engage enemy bombers from a distance beyond the range at which they can defend themselves with any conventional aircraft gun.

Recently some details have been given of one of the smallest missiles which is in production in the United States. This is indeed an air-to-air missile known as the Hughes FALCON (*Fig.* 6.2) which weighs a little over 100 lb (45 kg) and is still capable, as shown by Air Force tests, of destroying QB-17 and F-80 jet drones even without an explosive warhead and when these planes were manœuvring to simulate enemy bombers. Equipped with an explosive warhead, the FALCON is claimed as making every hit a sure kill. It is launched from interceptors several miles away from the target and it travels at supersonic speed, powered by a solid-propellant rocket engine. The launching aircraft is guided by radar to the firing position and when this is reached the missiles are fired automatically at the correct time to ensure certain interception. In fact Hughes Aircraft Company is building a system of fire control[8] which controls the aircraft from the instant it leaves the runway, guides it to the target, fires the FALCON and automatically returns the plane back to its home runway.

The Hughes FALCON was conceived by the United States Air Force for installation in interceptor aircraft. It was developed and produced by the Hughes Aircraft Company, Tucson, Arizona.[9] When the FALCON is launched from the interceptor plane which carries it, the missile seeks the target which has been pointed out to it. The electronic intelligence of the FALCON system is designed to hold it on course to hit the target despite any evasive manœuvres which the enemy bomber may make. The FALCON has been under development for the Air Force since 1947. Hughes Aircraft launched its first test rocket in 1950 and the weapon has since been hitting target drones out of the air even without explosive charges. Assistant Secretary to the United States Air Force, Trevor Gardner, emphasized that the successful development of the FALCON had pushed America's defence frontiers farther away from cities and homes and had increased the probability of destroying attacking bombers. He went so far as to say that he believed that the FALCON would be one of the most important contributions to the defence of the North American Continent against air attack since the development of radar, and he confirmed that the FALCON is designed for use by interceptors operating from bases in the Arctic regions many miles from the centres of the population.

In another statement Air Force Secretary Gardner said that he could not foresee the Air Force suddenly declaring a surplus of aircraft to be replaced by guided missiles. Rather he thought that guided missiles will assume their correct place as supplementing the growing arsenal of weapons, while air-to-air missiles would be used to increase the lethal power of manned aircraft. Tactical ballistic missiles would be used to supplement the abilities of tactical bombers, and when intercontinental ballistic missiles were developed they would supplement the deterrent power of the Strategic Air Command. He explained that the FALCON could be carried in a one-man or two-man interceptor aircraft.

It was claimed that the FALCON, together with the electronic

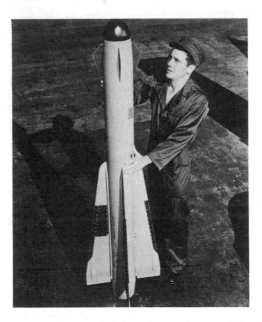

FIG. 6.2. (a) *The Hughes FALCON is the smallest guided missile in production in the United States. It is carried by interceptor aircraft which are guided electronically to the firing position at which the FALCON missiles are released and seek out their airborne targets.*

(Photo. U.S. Air Force)

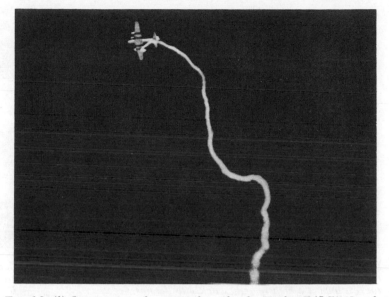

FIG. 6.2. (b) *Interception of a target drone by the Hughes FALCON rocket missile. In some tests drones have been destroyed even when the missile carried no explosive warhead.* (Photo. U.S. Air Force)

systems now carried in interceptor aircraft, gave the advantage to the defence in any engagement between the interceptor and the bomber.

The FALCON rocket is reported to be undergoing certain modifications, for example its blunt radome is being streamlined and different types of guidance are available. The solid-propellant system for the FALCON is reported to have been developed by the Thiokol Chemical Corporation (see *Fig.* 6.2a) who manufacture smokeless solid-propellants which are very useful in air-to-air missiles because the attacking pilot can have a clear vision of the interception. The rocket motor employed in FALCON develops a thrust of about 6,000 lb (2,700 kg) for a period of about 1 sec.

It appears that it is now possible to fit an atomic warhead into a projectile as small as 4 or 5 in (10–13 cm) in diameter.[10] This will, of course, give a tremendous defence potential to even the small fighter aircraft.

FIG. 6.3. (a) *The Fairey FIREFLASH is shown here in launching position mounted beneath the wing of an aircraft. Two large solid-propellant booster rockets impart a high velocity quickly to the missile.*

FIG. 6.3. (b) *Launching takes place from the wing-tip of the attacking aircraft when it comes within range of the radio-controlled target drone.*

170

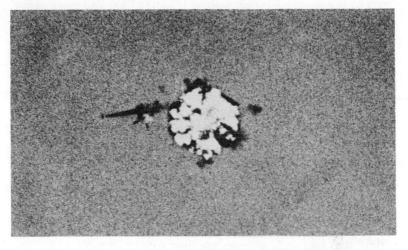

FIG. 6.3. (c) *The missile homes on the target and explodes its warhead automatically when it comes within lethal range of the target.*

FIG. 6.3. (d) *The interception is completed as the drone falls in flames and out of control.*

(Photos. Fairey Aviation Co. Ltd.)

While the present FALCON weighs 112 lb (51 kg) and costs about £3,000 to manufacture, a modified version will be slightly heavier at 120 lb (54 kg) weight.

In Britain the De Havilland Aircraft Company is reported[11] to be developing an infra-red seeking air-to-air missile, and photographs have, indeed, been released of one British missile being released from a Meteor aircraft during trials, but it was not revealed who was the manufacturer. The De Havilland missile will probably be propelled by a rocket motor using high test peroxide as oxidant. This is expected because the company has made some remarkable developments in this field for assisted take-off purposes, for example the SPRITE and the SUPER SPRITE.

However, due to the abnormal security regulations no details have been released of any British missiles or test vehicles. It is generally agreed that the most advanced British missile is in the air-to-air variety, and that these missiles are now coming into full-scale production. It is probable that it is these air-to-air missiles which a British statement at the ministerial meeting of the North Atlantic Council in December 1955 said would be available to the Western allies. However, it has been claimed (at the end of 1955) that no British fighter squadrons had received guided weapons, even though these weapons were in production. But the tempo of British guided missile effort is by no means as slow as is generally believed. We can gain an idea of the tremendous progress being made by considering such releases that the Fairey Aviation Company is producing an advanced air-to-air missile, which is going into initial limited production. It is known as the FIREFLASH and is powered by solid-propellant rockets. The English Electric Company has now in full operation at Stevenage a guided missile factory[12] and has been advertising for staff in connexion with celestial guidance systems.

It has been suggested[13] that the BOMARC forms part of the most recent idea of a guided weapon system which relies upon completely automatic defences. This arises following the revelation that the BOMARC can now be equipped with FALCON rockets. The idea would then be to use the very expensive long-range surface-to-air missile to carry the less expensive air-to-air missiles to within striking range of the target. When this has been reached, the air-to-air missiles would be discharged, while the long-range surface-to-air missile would make an attempt to return to base where it could be recovered, probably by a landing technique similar to that used with the large surface-to-surface missile known as the REGULUS.

The new air-to-air missile of the U.S. Navy is the SIDEWINDER which is reported to be produced at a cost of less than £400. The missile has been developed at Inyokern, and costs about one tenth of the other air-to-air missiles, namely the FALCON and the SPAR-ROW.[14]

France has two solid-propellant air-to-air missiles in production, the Matra R 051 and the SFECMAS 5501. Both appear to be boosted two-stage vehicles weighing about 350 lb (160 kg) and 280 lb (130 kg) respectively.

The Canadian air-to-air missile is known as VELVET GLOVE. Early versions were tested at the Cold Lake, Alberta 4,000 sq miles (10,000 sq km) weapon test range of the Defence Research Board Facility as long ago as 1953. Some of the new Canadian guided missiles have been developed by Avro Canada Limited.

A Soviet air-to-air missile is called the M-100, it has a diameter of about 10 in (25·4 cm) and is 13 ft (3·9 m) long. Its overall weight is 900 lb (408 kg) and its speed is supersonic. The sustaining motor is a solid-propellant rocket. Another Soviet air-to-air missile is the RS-82 which is a solid-propellant rocket about 3·25 in (8·25 cm) in diameter. This latter is probably an unguided rocket.

The efficiency of any guided missile defensive system depends upon an extensive radar network and most important upon receiving early warning. Although Britain now has a new radar chain which uses an improved type of radar,[15] this is only useful over fairly short ranges. The hundreds of underground units which cover the whole of the United Kingdom and check all objects travelling in the air are to be used for the automatic firing of missiles if it transpires that identification confirms an enemy. However, this is only a short range system and in Europe the situation is indeed very poor according to reports issued in December 1955. At that time it was claimed that Britain could only be certain of obtaining an early warning providing the attacking bombers came over Western Germany. As Britain would undoubtedly be the prime target of any attack, having as it does the great air fields for the deterrent atomic bombers of the Strategic Air Command, it is most important that early warning radar systems should be spread in a network over Europe. One analysis[16] of a guided missile interception has shown that the early warning must take place when the attacking planes are at least 300 miles (480 km) from the target, in fact 400 miles (650 km) would be much safer, when the flying time is about 40 min before the bombers could release their bombs. If the interceptors were alerted when the bombers were about 300 miles (480 km) away first interception with air-to-air missiles could be possible at a distance of just under 200 miles (320 km) from the target. If the attacking bombers evaded this interception, the ground-to-air missile sites would have to be alerted and would open fire at a range of 100 miles (160 km). While the missiles were moving from the launching sites to the bombers the latter would travel between 25 and 30 miles (40 and 48 km) so that the first missile interception would take place at only 75 miles (100 km) from the target. If nuclear warheaded bombs were being carried it can be seen that this is not a very healthy situation, and that if thermo-nuclear bombs exploded within 50 miles (80 km) of the target considerable damage could still result from the fall-out.[17]

It is obvious that with the increasing reliability of guided weapon systems, both ground-to-air and air-to-air, attacks by conventional bombers even when flying at supersonic speeds are going to become more and more hazardous. Military planners are, therefore, concentrating on the second type of airborne missile, that is, the one which is launched from an aircraft against a ground target at such a distance from that target that the mother plane can remain out of range of the target's defences. For this purpose it is necessary to use a high velocity vehicle which can evade the defensive missiles.

When, during World War II, the German Armies were almost at the limit of their advance in Russia and the Volga city of Stalingrad was threatened with capture, the Russians produced a weapon which was probably quite decisive. It was the rocket bomb which, with its accuracy and high impact velocity, was able to rout the armoured vehicles and tanks of the enemy. This weapon made the dive bomber obsolete and soon afterwards produced developments which became known as flying artillery.

The Russian rocket bomb was suspended under the wings of the Stormovik IL-2 fighter, two bombs being carried by each aircraft. The velocity of impact with the target was about 800 ft (244 m) per sec, which was quite sufficient to penetrate armoured vehicles and to destroy concrete gun emplacements.

Bombing with high impact velocities from low altitudes is made possible by employing rocket power to accelerate the bomb after its release from the attacking aircraft. Normally in order to obtain high impact velocities with ordinary bombs it is necessary to increase the altitude at which the aircraft is flying at the time of bomb release. But there are a number of difficulties. First, accuracy is reduced unless complicated sights are employed, and, secondly, a terminal speed is reached so that the technique is severely limited. Moreover, it results in a complicated trajectory for the missile, and hence accurate sighting and computing apparatus has to be carried in the aircraft. However, the high speed of the continuously accelerating rocket bomb not only straightens the path and improves accuracy of aim and ease of sighting, but also produces a high impact velocity even if release is made at comparatively low altitudes. The air-launched rocket projectile thus became an ideal weapon for use against heavily fortified positions such as gun emplacements, tanks, and armoured ships. In fact the weapon is ideal for attack against all those targets where normal bombs or cannon fire will not effect penetration or are not sufficiently accurate. When launched from an aircraft travelling at several hundreds of miles per hour, the aggregate efficiency of the rocket may well exceed that of a gun under similar circumstances.

The Western Allies were quick to recognize these points. Experiments started in Britain and in the United States and both countries did, indeed, employ rocket projectiles from February 1944. In point of fact Beaufighters, of the British Coastal Command, started using them even earlier than that date. Earlier still, however, in 1943, the Germans showed that they too had not been idle, by copying the Russian rocket-accelerated bomb and by using rocket shells which were fired from aircraft. These projectiles were employed by the Luftwaffe against the daylight raiding bombers of the United States Army Air Force. However, these latter are more accurately classed as air-to-air missiles which have been discussed earlier.

It was disclosed on the 25th May 1944 that four types of British aircraft, the Typhoon, Beaufighter, Hurricane, Swordfish, had been modified to carry rocket projectiles, officially designated as R.Ps. The original experiments with these weapons commenced in 1941 when workers at the Royal Aircraft Establishment began to develop aircraft missiles from the Z-gun projectiles.

Each aircraft was fitted with eight launching rails, four beneath each wing, from which the same number of rockets could be fired either in pairs or as a complete salvo of eight. The aircraft, of course, experiences no recoil with this type of weapon.

The projectile itself consisted of a slender tubular steel case 3·5 in (8·9 cm) in diameter and about 50 in (1·27 m) long, containing a cordite propelling charge. The shell-shaped explosive head, which was screwed to the body before the loading of the rocket on to the aircraft could be either of two main types. The 60 lb (27 kg) variety used with Typhoons was about 14 in (36 cm) long and 6 in (15·3 cm) in maximum diameter. Its smaller head used with Coastal Command aircraft, such as Beaufighters, was armour-piercing and was only about 8 in (20·3 cm) long and 3·5 in (8·9 cm) in diameter. A certain amount of stability was achieved by means of four square fins, approximately 200 sq in (1,290 sq cm) in area, riveted on to the cylindrical case near to the nozzle. Burning for a period of four or five seconds, these rockets attained speeds of 800 m.p.h. (1,300 km/hr).

Announcements were made in late 1944 that many types of American aircraft were also fitted to fire rocket projectiles. The preliminary experiments with these missiles were made about 1942 at Wright Field, and at the Aberdeen Proving Grounds, the aircraft employed being a Curtis P.40. Heavy steel tubes, attached under the wings, provided launching devices, but were later replaced by lightweight tubes of paper-base plastic. They were mounted below each wing in clusters of three, and each tube was 10 ft (3 m) in length and 4·5 in (11·4 cm) in diameter. The projectiles themselves were somewhat different from the British counterpart, the length being only about 3 ft (0.9 m), while their diameter was just under 4·5 in (11·4 cm). The projectiles were stabilized by rotation about their longitudinal axis thus helping to minimize dispersion which could arise from asymmetries of manufacture. Rotation was caused by air forces acting upon inclined fins at the tail of the rocket. These fins were folded while the rocket was in its launching tube and sprang open into position after firing.

But although these rocket projectiles took tremendous toll of German armour during the Normandy invasion and also were most effective throughout the island-hopping attack on Japan, producing such developments as the American TINY TIM, they were merely unguided missiles. Nowadays they are employed as air-to-air weapons to give fighter aircraft a tremendous fire power for the interception of subsonic bombers or for use against other fighters. During the concluding phases of World War II an attempt at guidance was made for missiles launched from the air to the ground.

The first use of an air-to-ground guided weapon was the German Hs.293,[18] commonly known as the rocket glider bomb. (*Fig.* 6.4.)

FIG. 6.4. *An early German air-to-surface missile was the Hs.293 which used a bi-propellant rocket motor underslung in a nacelle below the vehicle.*

In appearance very much like a small fighter aircraft, the Hs.293 was 11 ft 8 in (3·56 m) long, and the cylindrical fuselage was about 19 in (49 cm) in maximum diameter. The wing span was 9 ft 6 in (2.9 m) and the chord at the roots was 30 in (76 cm) tapering to 22 in (56 cm) at the tips. The forward portion of the aircraft contained an explosive head equal to that of a 1,000 lb (450 kg) bomb, while the rear part enclosed the electrical and radio apparatus by means of which the pilot of the aircraft could control the path of the bomb after it had been released and at distances of up to about 4·5 miles (7 km). Flares projected at the tail unit to assist this guidance. The rocket combustion chamber and associated propellant tanks were underslung in a nacelle below the main fuselage of the bomb. This nacelle was 7 ft 2 in (2·18 m) long and 14 in (35·6 cm) in diameter. It was suspended below the bomb by a three-legged support, which enabled its easy attachment to be made, there being a spring-loaded catch which snapped into place and firmly held the unit when it was mounted. On the attachment unit there were two grub screws, one near to the front bolt which supported the rocket unit and the other close to the front mounting pillars. These screws made it possible to adjust the angle which the unit made with respect to the bomb itself. The axis of the rocket motor was already inclined at an angle of 30 deg to the longitudinal axis of the unit, and the screws enabled final adjustment to be made so that the thrust line would pass through the centre of gravity of the missile and thereby assist stability.

The Hs.293 had an all-up weight at the time of leaving the parent aircraft of 1,730 lb (785 kg) of which 150 lb (68 kg) consisted of propellants. The rest of this weight was divided approximately as follows: warhead, 1,120 lb; engine, 1,140 lb; mainplane, 130 lb; tail unit and fuselage skin, 95 lb; and radio equipment, 95 lb (508, 517, 59, 43, 43 kg). Used in the Bay of Biscay and the Mediterranean from 1943 onwards, the bomb was very effective when it was first employed and had a measure of surprise. One of its most successful applications was against the ships which were landing troops and supplies at the Anzio and the Salerno beach-heads during the battle for Italy.

For several minutes the mother aircraft which was carrying the Hs.293 would circle the convoy while the controller picked out his target. The missile was then released when the aircraft was flying at a speed of about 200 m.p.h. (320 km/hr) and at a height of approximately 3,000 ft (914 m). The rocket propulsion unit came into operation, and burning for about 12 sec, with a maximum thrust of some 1,300 lb (590 kg), accelerated the bomb to a speed approaching 375 m.p.h. (600 km/hr). Deep penetration through the armour and the steel bulkheads of the vessels being attacked was made before the explosion took place, and tremendous damage was caused.

Because of its small size and high speed the bomb was extremely difficult to intercept once it had been launched. Fire from the attacked vessels was most ineffective, due to the smallness of the frontal area presented to the gunners. Providing that the pilot of the aircraft could maintain control of the missile, it was an effective weapon up to reasonably long ranges. However, radio control can be interfered with, despite security and anti-jamming circuits, and this was one important counter-measure. As the bomb came in rather low over the water shells were often fired into the sea in the path of the missile so that the resultant columns of water would deflect it from its target.

The most effective defence was, of course, the provision of fighter protection for convoys so that the parent aircraft could be either destroyed or forced to remain at a respectable distance from the convoy. Such a method of attacking a convoy would not be practical to-day due to guided missile defences which have ranges far exceeding the $4\frac{1}{2}$ miles of the old German glider bomb.

The projectile was visually guided to its objective by means of the tail flares, the frequency modulated radio control operated solenoid-actuated controls on the wing and tail surfaces and an Ascania gyroscope stabilizer was carried. The ailerons, operated by K.30 servo-units which were mounted in the wings and attached to the main tubular spar, had an area of 190 sq in (1,226 sq cm). Inspection of the servos and their adjustment could be made through panels on the upper surface of the wing.

The wing itself was constructed from metal, with a tubular main spar and conventional ribs. A sheet metal skin was attached by screws and could easily be removed for inspection purposes. The single elevator had an area of 248 sq in (1,600 sq cm), and was also solenoid operated. The electrical connexions between bomb and aircraft were made by a 12-pin plug and socket, and those between bomb and propulsion unit by means of a 2-pin plug and socket.

A destructor was fixed in the radio compartment on the starboard side of the bomb, quite close to the tuning window which was needed for the setting up of the radio equipment to the correct frequency. Power for the radio and electrical services was obtained from a battery mounted next to the filter unit aft of the explosive head.

The usual motor was the Walter 109–507 B which was a bi-propellant unit employing T-stoff and Z-stoff and which operated on the normal Walter cold cycle. Over 1,000 of these units were produced during World War II.[19] Operation of the rocket motor consisted of the electrical firing of a cartridge which ruptured a metal diaphragm and allowed pressurized air to displace the propellants from the tanks into the reaction chamber. The pressure air tanks were each 18 in (45·7 cm) long and 5·25 in (13·3 cm) in diameter. They were designed to be filled to a pressure of 200 atmospheres, but before installation they were tested to 300 atmospheres. Empty they each weighed just over 15·4 lb (7 kg) and they had a capacity of 1·56 gal (7·1 l). From these tanks the air was piped to the electrically operated valve in which the rupturing of a metal diaphragm by the gas pressure generated from the firing of a cartridge allowing air to pass to the other parts of the system. A gauge was taken from the valve and indicated the pressure of the air inside the air bottles. From the valve the pressurized air passed through another valve which reduced the pressure to about 33 atmospheres.

A distributing and non-return valve then metered the air to the two tanks, and it was so arranged that there was a slight delay of the air flow to the T-stoff tank and also a regulation of the pressure applied to that tank in order to prevent hard starts by a sudden influx of peroxide at 33 atmospheres pressure. The valve was a spring-loaded piston, operated by the air pressure and controlling the flow of air to the T-stoff tank but not to the Z-stoff tank.

The pressurized air then passed directly to the T-stoff tank, but through a non-return valve to the twin tanks which contained the permanganate. These two tanks were fabricated from welded steel sheet and were each 3·625 in (9·2 cm) in diameter and 8·25 in (21 cm) long, with a total capacity of 0·26 gal (1·18 l). When full, the two of them contained 7·5 lb (3·4 kg) of Z-stoff.

The T-stoff tank on the other hand was constructed of welded aluminium alloy. It was cylindrical in shape, with dished ends, being 28 in (71 cm) long and 12 in (34 cm) in diameter, and having a capacity of 11 gal (50 l). The weight of propellant carried in this tank was 132 lb (60 kg).

From these propellant tanks the feed lines passed along the port side of the motor to the reaction chamber. The T-stoff feed line was 1·2 in (3 cm) diameter light alloy tubing and proceeded directly from the tank to the injector at the head of the chamber, whereas the other line, constructed from 0·4 in (1·0 cm) diameter steel tubing, passed first through a filter before connecting with the orifice on the port side of the reaction chamber.

The reaction chamber itself was fabricated from welded steel sheet with walls of about 0·1 in (0·25 cm) thickness. It was 7 in (17·8 cm) in diameter and 11 in (27·9 cm) in length. A short expansion nozzle increased the overall length to 16 in (40·6 cm).

There was a flow reversal burner cup at the head of the chamber and helical guide vanes to increase the effective length of the combustion space. These vanes and the cup were supported by a central tube, and, in addition, four vanes in two planes at right angles to each other, but parallel to the axis of the motor, supported the internal arrangement at the nozzle throat. T-stoff was sprayed into the burner cup by a special injector. In this injector there was a double diaphragm of thin plastic, which was ruptured by the T-stoff pressure and prevented spilling of the propellants before the unit was ready to be started. The liquid then flowed into a chamber from which it was sprayed into the burner cup through several small holes. Z-stoff injection was accomplished through a simple orifice, and it was so arranged that the liquid impinged on a platform to promote turbulence and more complete combustion.

In operation the unit developed a peak thrust of 1,500 lb (680 kg) which decayed during the 12 sec run, and the propellant consumption was 34 lb per lb thrust hr. The specific impulse obtained from the propellant was 105 sec, and the pressure inside the reaction chamber rose to 18·4 atmospheres.

The Hs.293 was only one of a series of such missiles. Next in the series was the Hs.294 air-to-sea guided bomb, which was designed to enter the water some 200 ft (61 m) away from the target at a velocity of 200 m.p.h. (320 km/hr) to attack ships below the water line. It was considerably slowed down in its passage through the denser medium, so that its velocity of impact was much less than that of the Hs.293. The rocket unit employed was the Walter bi-propellant unit and had exactly the same weight and performance characteristics as the one of the Hs.293.

Three further experimental models, the Hs.295, Hs.296 and Hs.297, were under development but did not go into production. It is known that the Hs.296 was designed to use a television homing system invented by Dr Werner Rambushe.[20] The television device consisted of an iconoscope, which acted as the eye, suitable electrical circuits to interpret the signals received from the eye, and servos to direct the eye towards the target. Additional servos were used to operate the control surfaces of the missile and cause it to proceed in the direction indicated by the eye. This television homing system weighed about 5·5 lb (2·5 kg), had a size of about 8 in (20·3 cm) diameter and 8 in in length. A larger type was also being developed for application to other missiles in which specifications of size and weight were not so restricted. The unit was tested several times in aircraft and distinct vision of the target was given.

Later experimental versions of the Hs.293 included rocket propulsion units constructed by Schmidding of Bodenbach, and employing a more powerful propellant than the peroxide-permanganate combination. Hs.293 H was one of these later models which was series produced from March 1944 onwards. It employed an air-cooled motor, the 109–513, with propellants of gaseous oxygen and M-stoff (methanol) in the proportions by weight of 32 lb (14·5 kg) and 49 lb (22 kg) respectively. The all-up weight of the unit was 293 lb (133 kg) and the overall length was 88 in (223 cm) with a diameter of 13·8 in (35 cm). It was, however, only one of several improved rocket units designed for this type of missile.

The general arrangement of these components was very similar indeed to that of the 109-507. The methanol was contained in a large cylindrical tank in front of the unit, taking the place of the T-stoff tank. Instead of two compressed air bottles there were four in this unit and these were used to store the compressed oxygen at a pressure of 220 atmospheres being arranged in tandem banks of two. The reaction chamber was attached at the rear, inclined to the general axis of the motor, and was comparable in size and shape to that of the peroxide-permanganate chamber. Valves for the control of the unit were situated between the two banks of oxygen tanks, while propellant feed was obtained by using the reduced pressure of the oxygen to displace the methanol into the reaction chamber. The motor developed a thrust of 1,340 lb (608 kg) for 11 sec, with a specific propellant consumption of 20·7 lb per lb thrust hr. An improved specific impulse of 175 sec was thus achieved by the use of this propellant combination.

The Germans also had the Blohm and Voss anti-shipping glider bomb, which was launched from an aircraft but had no means of propulsion. The main feature of this bomb was that it used concrete wings with an exceptionally high aspect ratio. Although it was not radio controlled it had a gyroscopic stabilizer and a form of homing device.

A number of bombs which were radio controlled or wire controlled were included in an X-series of missiles. The FX.1400 radio-controlled high-level armour piercing bomb was used successfully against ships at Plymouth in early 1944. The bomb was dropped from an altitude of about 20,000 ft (6,100 m) and the mother aircraft kept in the line of sight with the bomb and the target. The radio controlling signals were sent to the bomb to keep it between the aircraft and the target until the target was hit.

The FX.1400 was steered by varying the drag produced by fins projecting across the airstream;[21] one pair operating at right angles to the other. They vibrated at a frequency of 5 cycles per sec and normally would project an equal amount on either side of the fin. The steering control increased the time of stay on one side, so that it would be greater than the other, thereby producing an asymmetric drag. It was claimed that this system avoided the high torque and control currents needed for conventional rudders. The radio controls themselves were straightforward devices using a radio frequency modulated by four or five audio frequencies. At the receiver in the bomb the audio frequencies were filtered, rectified, and used to operate relays. In order to prevent jamming, later control systems used a wire loop which consisted of about 6 miles (10 km) of wire paid out from containers on both the bomb and the aircraft. The steel wire was 0.001 in (0.2 mm) in diameter and was coated with an insulating oxide. It was claimed that from an altitude of 23,000 ft (7,000 m) the FX bomb could be landed within a circle of 1 km in diameter, but the requirements that the attacking plane must remain steadily above the bomb to guide it to the target made itself a sitting target for anti-aircraft defence.

The total weight of the bomb was just over 3,000 lb (1,360 kg), the steering, which has been described above, was accomplished by spoilers mounted in the cruciform fins of the tail. The overall length of the bomb was 130 in (3.30 cm) and the span of the cruciform surfaces amounted to 59 in (150 cm). The bomb carried a high explosive warhead weighing 595 lb (270 kg). This was known also as the XI armour-piercing bomb.

The X2 bomb had improved controls over the X1 and an X3 version later appeared having further improvements. The X5 was a heavier version of the X3 weighing about 2·5 tons, whereas X6 was a special version of X5 designed to give maximum blast effects. X7 was a wire-controlled missile which was designed for use against armoured fighting vehicles at ranges of under 100 yds (100 m). This missile was rocket propelled, it was about 30 in (75 cm) in length and weighed 20 lb (9 kg) with a warhead weighing 5·5 lb (2·5 kg). The missile had only one control surface which was offset from the longitudinal axis by about 20 in (50 cm) to avoid interference from the rocket jet in the tail.

The maximum speed attained by the X7 was only about 220 m.p.h. (350 km/hr) and although in general outline it was similar to the X4 described earlier in this chapter and wire-control was again employed, it only had one set of fins equipped with spoilers. Development and testing had not been completed by the end of the war.

Most of the experimental models which were tested, employed the 109-506 motor. This was a solid-propellant unit which used diglycol-dinitrate in two stages, each of which contained 7 lb (3·2 kg) of propellants, moulded by Wasag. Stage one developed an initial thrust of 152 lb (69 kg) but this decayed during the run of 2 to 3 sec to 11 lb (5 kg), and the total impulse from the stage amounted to 176 lb sec (80 kg sec). Stage two was triggered by the first and continued for a further 8 sec with a thrust remaining at 11 lb (5 kg) thus producing a total impulse of 88 lb sec (40 kg sec).

In the United States too during the concluding phases of the war a number of air-to-ground missiles were developed (*Fig. 6.5*), and in fact were used operationally. One of these was the 1,000 lb (450 kg) bomb known as AZON. The United States Navy also had a missile known as the BAT which carried a 1,000 lb (450 kg) warhead. This was claimed to have a range of about 14 miles (24 km) and a speed of 400 m.p.h. (650 km/hr). The BAT was a pure glide bomb, it was not radio controlled but it used a homing device installed in the nose radome. It was a high winged aircraft with conventional tail unit using two rudders. A similar missile was the Air Force GB-8 which was equipped with a television eye and was also radio controlled. A further United States Navy missile was the GARGOYLE, which was a rocket-propelled bomb. It was radio controlled and also used a homing device. A free-falling bomb with a circular wing was known as the American ROC; which was equipped with a television eye and appears as a development of the X1, being a high angle bomb.

A modern missile which seems to follow the pattern of the X-series is the French SFECMAS wire-controlled SS 10, which has a range of about 2 miles (3 km). It is a small projectile which is guided by wire and is designed for attacking objects on the ground, especially in anti-tank warfare when it is fitted with a shaped charge. The SS 10 can be launched from a very short ramp or from its shipping crate. The ramp can be mounted on a truck, aircraft or helicopter. The trajectory is controlled by a controller who is sometimes called the pilot. He relies on radar, with the aid of which he directs the missile

FIG. 6.5. *A typical air-launched missile is this NACA vehicle designed for research purposes. This photograph shows the supersonic wings and the instrumentation mounted in the nose section. An operation missile would be able to dispense with most of these instruments and the space would be available for a warhead.*

(Photo. N.A.C.A. Ames Aeron. Lab.)

towards the target both in direction and height. The transmission of the controlling impulses to the missile is obtained by means of two wires paid out from the missile. The SS 10 is expected to have 80 per cent success in kills during normal operations. It has cruciform wings with a wing span of 30 in (75 cm). The overall length of the missile is 34 in (86 cm) and its weight is 33 lb (15 kg). A training simulator is reported as available in which the missile is represented by a spot on a cathode-ray tube. This spot reacts to control impulses as would a real missile. The target is also represented by another luminous spot on the tube.[22]

The existence of the interceptor missiles which have been described earlier means, of course, that in order to deliver their loads safely, bombers must remain as far as possible from the target area and yet still be able to deliver their bombs accurately. Hence, instead of relying upon the normal gravity drop for delivery, the bombs themselves have essentially to become guided missiles. Several aircraft may be used to give a beacon pattern around the target. The missile is dropped, uses rocket boost to accelerate to high speeds and to make interception difficult, and then is guided from the mother plane, finally using its own electronic brain, sensing on the three beacons, for homing on the target.

Such missiles quite obviously must come into the top secret category, and accordingly very little information has been released concerning modern developments. The French Société Matra had an air-launched missile, the M.04, but this has now been developed as a surface-to-air weapon. It used a liquid-propellant rocket motor, which developed a thrust of 2,750 lb (1,250 kg) for 14 sec, to reach a speed of between Mach 1 and 2. The missile was about 15 ft (4·6 m) long and 16 in (40·6 cm) in diameter, and weighed 770 lb (349 kg) dry, and 1,020 lb (463 kg) at launching when complete with propellants. It was winged and could accordingly glide some distance after the rocket motor attained all-burnt. The company is now working on more advanced projects details of which are not yet revealed.

Fairchild have announced that they are manufacturing the PETREL, an anti-submarine missile powered by a turbo-jet which develops 1,000 lb (454 kg) thrust for a dry weight of 300 lb (136 kg). This vehicle has a range of about 20 miles (32 km). In November 1955 it was announced that the cruciform-winged PETREL was entering the operational stage of its development. Fairchild are also working on a new missile for the Navy known as GOOSE.

Eastman-Kodak are producing an air-to-underwater weapon known as DOVE. It is equipped with a homing device for use against submarines. One version used for air-to-surface is reported to be fitted with an infra-red homing device.

The Glenn L. Martin Company had a development missile known as the BULLPUP the latest reports of which say that under the name of BULLDOG this will be used as an air-to-surface missile. The propulsion of this missile is by means of a solid-propellant rocket and the missile has an overall length of 11 ft (3·35 m) and a diameter of 12 in (30·4 cm).

But the most ambitious project appears to be that of Bell Aircraft who are producing the RASCAL, which is really a long-range missile for air-to-ground operation. It appears to have been developed from experience gained from the X1 series of research aircraft (*Fig.* 6.6), and is designed to be carried in the bomb bay of a B-36 or B-50 like the X1, or the newer bombers such as the B-52 or B-58, and to be released at a distance of about 100 miles (160 km) from the target. It is rocket propelled and travels at Mach 2·5, being guided to the target by a pre-set programme and by radar. Both the rocket engine and the airframe are developed by the Bell Aircraft Corporation. The missile will be released at about 50,000 ft (15,000 m) altitude and will use its liquid-oxygen rocket motor to double this altitude and thus make interception difficult in the present state of ground-to-air missile development. At the target it may release a target seeking missile and itself return, or it may plunge to destroy the target by a warhead carried within it. The choice will depend upon the depth of the target in enemy held territory.

In Britain it may be assumed that this class of missile is also being developed, though no details of such weapons have been released.

It is concluded, therefore, that now that guided missiles are in the course of full-scale production, so that established launching sites should be common within the next decade, missions by conventional bombers will be extremely hazardous, a fact which is fully realized by military planners in all countries. Tactical missiles are accordingly being developed to replace the bombers. Over short ranges this is not proving a difficult task, and these types will be discussed in the next chapter in this book. But for long-range work the large bomber

FIG. 6.6. *Bell Aircraft Corporation is producing an air-to-surface missile which can be carried by bombers and then released about* 100 *miles from the target. Powered by rocket motors it can then climb to avoid interception before diving at high speed on to the target. It is possible that the design of the missile might follow the techniques developed from the X-series of research aircraft, one of which is shown in this photograph together with the mother plane which has carried it to the base of the stratosphere for launching.*

(Photo. Bell Aircraft Corporation)

still remains supreme. The main difficulty is that although it can reach its target, it is not likely to be able to approach near enough to deliver its bomb load safely, unless that load consists of some kind of self-propelled missile. Development of better interceptors will then reduce the effectiveness of even these attacking missiles. The solution appears to be to move to intercontinental missiles which follow orbits through space beyond the atmosphere and descend so quickly upon their objective that defence becomes difficult or impossible. But although the technical difficulties confronting the designers of these long-range missiles are immense, ultimately they will be surmounted.

TABLE 6.1 — *Air-to-Air Missiles*

Code: SP.R Solid-propellant rocket.
  LP.R Liquid-propellant rocket.

Name	X-4	Firebird	—	Falcon	Sparrow	Fireflash
Manufacturer	Ruhrstall	Ryan	—	Hughes	Sperry	Fairey
Propulsion	LP.R	LP.R	SP.R	SP.R	SP.R	SP.R
Booster	none	SP.R	none	none	none	2 × SP.R
Length, ft	6·2	7·5	13	6	8	6?
Length, m	1·85	2·3	4	1·8	2·4	1·8
Max. diam., in	9	6	?	6	6	?
Max. diam., cm	23	15·2	?	15·2	15·2	?
Wing span, ft	2·38	3·0	—	none	2·25	?
Wing span, m	0·72	0·91	—		0·68	?
Range, miles	1·8	?	?	4	4	?
Range, km	2·8	?	?	6·4	6·4	?
Speed	Subsonic	Mach 2	Supersonic	Mach 3	Mach 3	Supersonic
Control system	Wire	Command and homing	?	Radar homing	Beam rider and homing	Beam rider and homing
Launching, lb	132	600	900	100	500	?
Weight, kg	60	270	400	45	220	?
Status	Development	Production	Production	Production	Production	Production
Country	Germany	U.S.A.	U.S.S.R.	U.S.A.	U.S.A.	U.K.

TABLE 6.2 — *X-Series of Missiles*

Designation	Use	Propulsion	Weight pounds	kg
X-1	Armour-piercing bomb	none	3,000	1,360
X-2	Development of X-1	none	3,000	1,360
X-3	Further development	none	3,000	1,360
X-4	Air-to-air weapon	109–548	132	60
		109–603		
X-5	Heavy armour-piercing bomb	none	5,500	2,500
X-6	Development of X-5	none	5,500	2,500
X-7	Air-to-ground weapon	109–506	20	9

TABLE 6.3   *Air-to-Ground Missiles*

Code: LP.R Liquid-propellant rocket.
SP.R Solid-propellant rocket.

Name	FX1400	Hs.293	SS10	Petrel	Rascal	Bulldog
Manufacturer	Ruhrstall	Henschell	Sfecmas	Fairchild	Bell	Martin
Propulsion	none	LP.R	SP.R	Turbo-jet	LP.R	SP.R
Length, ft	11	11·75	3	24	20	11
Length, m	3·35	3·57	1	8	6·1	3·3
Max. diam., in	59	19	6	24	?	12
Max. diam., cm	150	48	15·2	61	?	30·4
Control	Radio or wire	Various	Wire	Radio and homing	Pre-set programme and radar	?
Speed	Supersonic	Subsonic	Supersonic	Subsonic	Mach 2·5	Supersonic
Range, miles	6	4·5	2	?	100	?
Range, km	9·8	7·2	3	?	160	?
Launching, lb	3,000	1,730	33	1500	?	?
Weight, kg	1,360	790	15	680	?	?
Type	Free-fall bomb	Winged	Winged	Cruciform-winged, air to underwater	Winged	?
Status	Operational	Operational	Production	Development	Development	Development
Country	Germany	Germany	France	U.S.A.	U.S.A.	U.S.A.

REFERENCES

[1] BURCHARD, J. E., *Rockets Guns & Targets*, Sect. III, Little, Brown & Co., 1949.
[2] BURGESS, E., *The Engineer*, 184, 10 Oct. 1947, 332.
[3] MULLER, F., *Lietfaden der Ferlenkung*, Deutsche Radar Verlagsgesellschaft mbH., 1955.
[4] BURGESS, E., *The Engineer*, 184, 17 Oct. 1947, 356.
[5] GARTMANN, H., *Weltraumfahrt*, No. 1, Jan. 1951, 11–16.
[6] GATLAND, K. W. G., *Jnl. Brit. Interplan. Soc.*, 9, 4, July 1950, 189–90.
[7] MINISTRY OF SUPPLY, *Press Release* No. 6, London, 22 Aug. 1953.
[8] HUNTER, F. S., *American Aviation*, 19, 11, 24 Oct. 1955, 147–9.
[9] U.S. DEPT. OF DEFENCE, Office of Public Information, *Official Release* No. 247–55, Washington, D.C., 15 Mar. 1955.
[10] ANON., *Jet Propulsion*, 25, 9, Part I, Sept. 1955, 473.
[11] ANON., *Inter Avia*, 10, 5, May 1955, 314–15.
[12] *Financial Times*, 24 Nov. 1955, p. 1.
[13] SMITH, J. F., *Inter Avia*, 10, 5, May 1955, 300–9.
[14] ZAEHRINGER, A. J.; BAKER, N. L., *Jet Propulsion*, 25, Nov. 1, 1955, 646.

[15] *Financial Times*, 2 Mar. 1955.
[16] PORTER, H. H., *Aeronautical Engin. Review*, **12**, 7, July 1953, 24–29.
[17] *Nuclear Weapons*, H.M.S.O., London, Jan. 1956.
[18] BURGESS, E., *The Engineer*, **184**, 3 Oct. 1947, 308–10.
[19] WALTER, H., *Jet Propulsion*, **24**, 3, May–June 1954, 166–71.
[20] BURGESS, E., *The Engineer*, **184**, 17 Oct. 1947, 256–358.
[21] BURNS, R. E., *et al.*, *CIOS Report*, XXII/88 Item 197, 10 May 1948.
[22] *Proc. European Assoc. for Research & Applic. of Rocket Aircraft & Rocket Engines*, Paris, 14–15 Oct. 1955.

CHAPTER VII

GROUND-TO-GROUND MISSILES

◎

THE POTENTIALITIES of the smaller guided missiles as destroyers of conventional aircraft have made it necessary for military planners to consider the use of long-range weapons other than bombers. There is no doubt that the German V-2 rocket, the forerunner of all ground-to-ground ballistic missiles, was a great technical achievement, but whether or not the use of skilled manpower for its development was justified is a matter which only historians are likely to settle. There are definite doubts about the matter, and it is felt by a number of strategists that Germany might have fared better in the war had such a large proportion of scientific manpower not been diverted to the guided missile field.[1] On the other hand had these weapons been developed before Germany risked the aggressions which led to the second World War, the outcome might have been very different from what it was. There is, however, no doubt that any nation must now be regarded as completely out of date from the military standpoint if long-range guided weapons are not included in its armoury.

Long-range weapons take two main forms; winged missiles travelling at near sonic velocities over ranges of 200 to 500 miles (320 to 800 km) which are used mainly for tactical purposes and the use of ballistic flight trajectories for projectile type vehicles which may have ranges of 20 miles (32 km) up to thousands of miles. In the former category was the wartime V-1 flying bomb but the low speed, relative short range and cumbersome launching ramp limited its usefulness. Nowadays there are several new American winged missiles which overcome these shortcomings. These include the Martin MATADOR and the Chance Vought REGULUS. Ground-to-ground missiles can be conveniently divided also into two categories; tactical missiles which are used up to ranges of 500 miles (800 km) and strategic missiles for intercontinental use. Both categories of missile include the winged and the ballistic types of vehicle.

Nowadays it is fully appreciated that danger of surprise aggression lies mainly in the intercontinental missile. We know that Russian rocket scientists are also aware of this fact and that they have considerably improved on the V-2 rocket.[2] On the other hand the West did not extend earlier German work but preferred to start out afresh, finding out from first principles. This is a serious criticism of Western policy raised to the author by a top German expert now working in the United States. Accordingly it is concluded that we may be behind Soviet developments in the field of long-range missiles.

At the present time the United States have at least three intercontinental missiles under accelerated development. These are the North American NAVAHO which uses rockets and ramjets and has a range of about 5,000 miles (8,000 km), the Northrop SNARK, turbojet powered for a 4,000 mile (6,400 km) range, and the Convair ATLAS which may have a range of about 5,000 miles (8,000 km). Each of these missiles is claimed by the United States Department of Defence to have intercontinental atomic capacity but differing design characteristics, both ballistic and winged missiles being represented.

As far as Britain is concerned there has been only scattered implications of interest in long-range vehicles. It is most likely that the tremendous expense of a development programme for intercontinental missiles will cause Britain, for the time being at least, to rely upon the work that is going on across the Atlantic. Staff advertisements for scientific personnel would indicate, however, that at least one British company has a long term project of this kind in hand, but it is likely that developments will be of winged rather than ballistic missiles. There have, however, been claims that Britain has perfected a 1,500 miles (2,400 km) range rocket vehicle but no details have been forthcoming.

At the present rate of guided weapon progress we are probably seeing the last generation of manned war aircraft, and even these are now becoming mere missile carriers. Modern fighters become increasingly large, complex and expensive, while the training of air crews becomes more and more difficult. It is unlikely that time will be available in any future emergency for the selection and training of sufficient men to fly an effective air force of piloted interceptors, especially when it is remembered that such a force must have a strength capable of preventing *all* attackers from penetrating the defences. At the same time the great atom bombers are themselves becoming too complex and too great a responsibility for air crews to have long operational lives even during peacetime.[3]

Once again, as with the other missiles, in order to get a historical background it is desirable to begin with reference to the German developments; first in the field of the 'buzz bomb' and secondly in the activities at Peenemünde which led to the production of the German A4 rocket.

On the 13th day of June 1944 the first operational long-range guided weapon exploded in Southern England. This was the FZG-76, the V-1 flying bomb.[4] Basically the missile was a small aeroplane catapulted from a special launching device and then steered on a pre-determined course to its target. The launching catapult consisted of eight steel sections joined end to end, the bomb being mounted on rails which ran along the top of them. A hollow cylinder passed through the length of the catapult, and hydrogen peroxide, decomposed by calcium permanganate, generated gas pressure which forced a piston along the cylinder. There was a self-sealing slit in the top of the firing cylinder through which the driving connexion was made by an engagement lug between the piston and a slot in the bomb. The V-1 was accelerated along the launching catapult for a distance of 157 ft (47·8 m) before it reached its launching speed of about 245 m.p.h. (400 km/hr). After launching the bomb climbed under the influence of its pulse-jet motor, while the piston fell clear of the bomb at the end of the launching ramp. The V-1 was guided by an auto pilot which consisted of three air-driven gyroscopes operating rudder and elevator control surfaces. The auto pilot was driven by air which was carried in two spherical wire-wound vessels. A pitch-azimuth gyro was monitored by a remote magnetic compass housed in the wooden nose of the bomb. This magnetic compass was adjusted before launching by means of a system of compensating magnets. The other two gyroscopes controlled the elevator and the rudder surfaces respectively. Control was effected through pneumatic relays, the movements of which deflected small air jets and allowed the compressed air supply to operate the servomotors of the control surfaces. Altitude of flight was controlled by a barometric device which consisted of a simple aneroid box which was adjusted prior to take-off so that any deviation from a pre-determined air pressure would cause the pitch-regulating gyroscope to be monitored and make the bomb fly at the correct altitude. The duration of flight of the V-1, and hence its range, was controlled by a windmill device at the nose.

Propulsion was by the Argus Rohr pulse-jet unit which burned petrol and gave a thrust of about 500 lb (226 kg) at 400 m.p.h. (640 km/hr). The range of the bomb was about 190 miles (350 km). The power unit consisted of a mild steel tube 11 ft 5 in (3·48 m) in length and having a maximum diameter of just over 21·5 in (54·6 cm). The nozzle diameter was 15·75 in (40 cm) and the thickness of the steel used was just over 0·1 in (0·25 cm). The all-up weight of the power unit was 360 lb (163 kg) and that of the bomb itself 8,000 lb (3,629 kg). The combustion chamber section of the tube was 3·5 ft (1·1 m) long and the nozzle 7 ft (2·1 m) long. At the forward end of the tube the air inlet grid contained a series of non-return flap valves constructed of carbon steel. There were also nine injection nozzles which were connected to the main fuel pipes. Pressure points in the inlet grid connected with the fuel valve control so that fuel would be injected at the correct stage of the combustion cycle. Fuel was admitted at a pressure of about 6 atmospheres and the fuel/air mixture was of a ratio of about 15 to 1. The bomb was constructed almost entirely of mild steel except for the wooden wings which were detachable and were easily assembled prior to firing, being attached on to tubular steel main spars.

When first used this bomb was a surprise weapon and was devastating in its effects. However, its low speed of 400 m.p.h. (640 km/hr) enabled new British jet fighters to destroy it, and as the attack continued the effects of the V-1 were minimized.* This method of pulse-jet propulsion is now used fairly extensively for target drones but not for operational guided missiles.

As far as ballistic ground-to-ground missiles are concerned German development was divided into two sections. First rocket- and ramjet-assisted shells fired from normal guns and secondly pure rocket projectiles.

Experiments had been made with shells which could be fired from a normal type of gun, but which contained rocket motors capable of considerably extending their range. Work on this type of projectile had been begun by the Germans several years before the outbreak

---

*Some of these missiles were used as air-to-ground weapons and were launched from aircraft against cities of N.W. England.

of war, but although successful tests were made, these missiles were never used operationally. It is thought, however, that certain large emplacements in the Pas de Calais area were being made for use with missiles of this nature.

It is known that the development produced a ramjet shell which employed zinc ethyl plus benzine or carbon disulphide as a fuel and atmospheric air as the oxidizer. Known as the Tromsdorff-Geschoss,[5] the shell was essentially a supersonic ramjet-driven, gun-fired projectile, which by its design could travel five times as far as another shell of the same calibre. It was projected by means of a standard rifled gun, and the larger versions had extreme ranges approaching 280 miles (450 km).

Long-range rocket projectiles mainly consisted of the A-series developed at Peenemünde, but Rheinmetal-Borsig also produced a four-stage ground-to-ground rocket which found operational use before the end of the war. About a score of these projectiles, which were known as the RHEINBOTE,[6] were, indeed, directed against Antwerp during the last winter of the second World War, but they proved to be most inaccurate.

RHEINBOTE was designed to operate at subsonic velocities up to a maximum range of 100 miles (160 km). At the time of launching the missile weighed 3,300 lb (1,500 kg) and had a total length of 472 in (12 m) and a maximum diameter of 16 in (40·6 cm). The propellant used was a solid, most probably diglycol-dinitrate and the warhead weighed about 88 lb (40 kg). One version was designed for launching from a gun barrel in order to extend the range and improve the accuracy.

The best-known missile of the A-series, some details of which are given in the table, was the V-2 rocket, officially known as the A4. The first rocket of the series was constructed as early as 1933.[7, 8] This was designated A1 and was designed to be directly stabilized by one large gyroscope which weighed 88 lb (40 kg) and which was situated at the nose of the rocket. The overall length of the rocket was 55 in (140 cm) and the body had a maximum diameter of 12 in (30·4 cm). The propellants used were liquid oxygen and alcohol with a total weight of 88 lb (40 kg) and propellant feed was by compressed nitrogen. Launching was to be vertically from a table, but only proving stand tests were made and no free flights took place. In the following year, however, two A2 rockets were fired.[9] They were similar to the A1, except that the gyroscope was moved from the nose to the centre of the missile. Successful vertical launches were achieved with the rockets rising to a height of 7,500 ft (2,280 m).

In 1938 a further model, A3, was constructed. This was a much larger rocket, being 300 in (762 cm) long and having a maximum diameter of 30 in (76·2 cm). Not only was the weight of propellants carried increased to 1,000 lb (450 kg), but also an increase in the specific impulse was obtained; one of 167 sec resulting as compared with the 143 sec of the early rockets. It was very similar in shape to the A4 and had auto steering with rudders in the gas stream. It was launched vertically, but only operated at subsonic velocities, whereas the next model, A5, which was constructed about the same time, and had the same dimensions and weight, was the prototype of the A4 and was designed to exceed the velocity of sound. It was, moreover, the first model to employ graphite vanes in the jet. A5 had a maximum range of 11 miles (16 km), and hundreds of these missiles were fired between 1938 and 1942 in order to investigate control, stability, and aerodynamic problems associated with rockets travelling at supersonic velocities.

The overall length of the A4[10, 11] was 46 ft 11 in (14·3 m) and the maximum body diameter 5 ft 5·5 in (1·66 m). The total weight of the rocket was 12·7 tons which included a warhead of 2,150 lb (975 kg), propellants amounting to 8·9 tons, and structure and power units of 6,750 lb (3,060 kg). At the nose of the rocket was the warhead, behind which was the control compartment containing an auto pilot, batteries and electrical equipment. After this was the alcohol tank and then the tank for the liquid oxygen. A motor compartment and tail fairing to which were attached four stabilizing fins contained a turbine and pump unit and the main combustion chamber and exhaust nozzle.

The body of the rocket was made from steel sheet riveted to stringers while the propellant tanks were welded from light alloy sheeting. The combustion chamber was fabricated from welded steel plate.

Thrust developed by the rocket motor amounted to about 26 tons weight and the propellants were driven through the rocket motor by means of two centrifugal pumps which were operated by a steam turbine, the steam being derived from the decomposition of concentrated hydrogen peroxide. Cooling of the combustion chamber and the nozzle was regeneratively obtained by circulating the alcohol through a cooling jacket. The flight to a range of 200 miles (320 km) took only 5 min. The rocket motor itself fired for 60 sec then the missile travelled along a ballistic trajectory. At the top of its roughly parabolic path its height above the Earth's surface was about 60 miles (96 km). Maximum velocity was reached at the time of completion of combustion of the propellants (time of burn-out) at an altitude of about 25 miles (40 km) and was about 3,500 m.p.h. (5,600 km/hr). This speed was again reached on the downward leg of the trajectory just before the missile re-entered the dense atmosphere. Then air resistance slowed it down so that impact velocity with the target was only 2,000 m.p.h. (3200 km/hr). The pre-determined path was obtained by using an internal memory and special gyroscopes which controlled four carbon vanes, which dipped into the exhaust jet, and four air vanes on the tips of the fins. A set of two of both types of vane acted as elevators to control the pitch of the rocket and gradually to tilt it so that at burn-out it was travelling at an angle of 45 deg to the horizontal. The other two sets of vanes moved together to control direction, that is the plane of the trajectory, or in opposition to stop the rocket from rolling about its longitudinal axis.

Experiments with a final version of the V-2 commenced in July 1942 and three months later the first successful launching was made when a rocket flew a distance of 170 miles (280 km). By two years later over 6,000 V-2 rockets had been constructed. In an underground factory at Nordhausen facilities were available for the completion of thirty rockets every day.

The first V-2 rocket was fired against London from Wassenaar, a small town near to the Hague, on 8th September 1944. By the close of hostilities over 2,000 rockets had been fired against London and 1,600 against Antwerp. It has been reported that 58 per cent of all missiles launched were effective though not all of them landed close to the intended target.

A6 was a design for a subsonic project which did not pass beyond the drawing office stage, while A7, constructed in 1941, was an A5 with wings. But perhaps the most interesting part of all the German rocket development was that concerned with the A9 and A10 projects, for A9 was designed as a winged, man-carrying rocket, while A10 was to be a huge booster weighing over 80 tons.

The greater part of the construction of the A9 was to be the same as in the A4, but, in addition, arrangements were to be made for the incorporation of a pressurized cabin instead of the warhead, for a retractable undercarriage, and for 150 sq ft (14 sq m) of wing area. The crew of one man would have had hand controls and been able to land the rocket at a velocity of only 300 m.p.h. (480 km/hr). At the time of exhaustion of the propellants the velocity of the A9 would be 4,270 ft per sec (1,300 m/sec), and a maximum height of 95,000 ft (29,000 m) was expected. Entering the denser regions of the atmosphere, the rocket would glide finally to land 17 min after launching at a distance of 370 miles (600 km) from the launching point.

The ultimate development, however, was to have been the use of the A10 booster with the A9 winged rocket, thus making possible ranges of 3,000 miles (4,800 km) and a maximum velocity of 9,200 ft per sec (2,800 m/sec) with an apex to the trajectory of 900,000 ft (275,000 m). The booster would have had a dry weight of 55,000 lb (25,000 kg) and, using 136,000 lb (62,000 kg) of liquid oxygen with methanol and water, it would have produced a total impulse of 22,000,000 lb sec (10,000,000 kg sec). It would have had an overall length of 315 in (8 m) and a maximum diameter of 138 in (3·5 m). The design assumed that it would be jettisoned at a velocity of about 3,900 ft per sec (1,180 m/sec) and then be recovered by means of a large parachute.

As part of the A9 programme two A4s were equipped with wings and launched. The first failed, but in January 1945 the other reached a speed exceeding Mach 4.

In 1945 the United States Army Ordnance Corps assigned the General Electric Company the task of firing a number of captured German V-2 rockets.[12] Initially, the programme called for the firing of twenty-five V-2s, but before the programme had been completed a total of sixty-seven were in fact launched.

The first V-2 was launched at the White Sands, New Mexico, Proving Grounds by engineers of the General Electric Company on 16th April 1946, and the programme was completed when the sixty-seventh was fired on 29th October 1951. Sixty-eight per cent of the launchings and subsequent flights were considered successful though not all of the rockets flew as planned. (*Fig.* 7.1.)

Originally designed to carry a 2,200 lb (1,000 kg) payload, the V-2s were carrying 47 per cent more than that by the time the series

FIG. 7.1. *The V-2 rocket was the first long-range ballistic missile and gave the attacker a tremendous advantage over the defences which still has not been lost. This photograph shows the launching of one of the V-2s which were tested in the United States, sixty-seven being fired by the General Electric Company for the U.S. Army Ordnance.*

(Photo. General Electric Company)

of tests concluded. A considerable number of the V-2s were modified for special experiments and as test vehicles for components of newly developed and designed missiles. Included in these components were a General Electric flight control system and a General Electric telemetering system, both of which were used in later HERMES missiles and adapted by other missile projects.

Also included in the V-2 tests were special projects and programmes for the gathering of specific data on rocket application and launching problems. Among them were the Bumper Programme, Operation Sandy, Operation Pushover, and Operation Blossom. In the Bumper Programme[13] a WAC CORPORAL missile was attached to the nose of a V-2. (*Fig.* 7.2.) After the V-2 burned out, the Corporal fired and ascended higher under its own power. One of these two-stage missiles reached a velocity of 5,000 m.p.h. (8,000 km/hr) and a height of 242 miles (487 km), the fastest and highest any man-made object had gone up to that date.

Operation Sandy was carried out in conjunction with the United States Navy. In this operation a V-2 was launched from the deck of the aircraft carrier USS *Midway*. The main concern in this operation was what would happen if the missile should topple on to the deck during launching. Sandy was a success, and the V-2 was launched. Although the rocket did tumble after launching and fell into the sea after breaking up into three parts, it proved the possibility of launching large rockets at sea. A Martin VIKING rocket was, indeed, fired to 106 miles (170 km) later in Operation Reach from the USS *Norton Sound*.

Operation Pushover was also conducted by General Electric engineers at the request of the United States Navy. In this programme determination was made as to the effect of the missile exploding during launching operations on a warship. The purpose of Operation Blossom was upper atmosphere research. Information as to the composition of the upper atmosphere, temperatures and pressures at high altitudes, cosmic ray research, voltage breakdown of electrical equipment, and other valuable data, all necessary for the design of long-range ballistic missiles, were obtained in this programme.[14]

In addition to conducting the V-2 tests General Electric engineers were designing and developing new missiles. In 1950 the first of the General Electric designed missiles was launched at White Sands.[15]

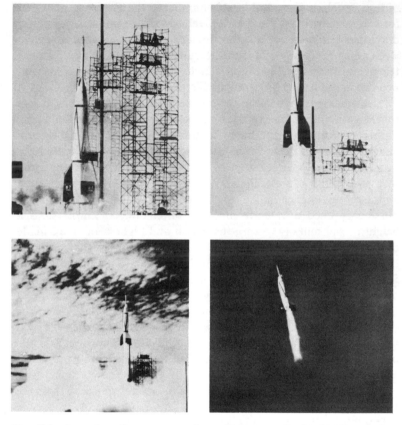

FIG. 7.2. *A number of two-stage rocket vehicles were fired in* 1949 *to perfect methods of separation of the stages and the starting of rocket motors at extreme altitudes. One of these BUMPER-WAC vehicles reached a speed of* 5,000 *miles an hour and a height of nearly* 250 *miles.*

(Photo. General Electric Company)

Given the designation HERMES A1 (*Fig.* 7.3) it was smaller than the V-2 and was designed as an anti-aircraft missile. A series of these missiles was launched during the following years. Later the A1 was modified for use as a surface-to-surface test vehicle. The first HERMES A1 was launched in May 1950 from White Sands, it was based on the design of the German WASSERFALL anti-aircraft weapon. It had four mid-section wings for fast manœuvrability. The aerodynamic shape of the HERMES A1 was adapted to save expensive wind tunnel time and so enable the engineers to take full advantage of the earlier and extensive German research. The propulsion and the flight control systems were, however, completely new designs by the General Electric Company. Propellants used in the rocket engine were liquid oxygen and alcohol and the rocket motor developed a sea level thrust exceeding 10,000 lb (4,500 kg). The overall length of the missile was 25·5 ft (7·7 m), its diameter was 2 ft 10 in (·86 m) and the wing span was 8 ft 2 in (2·5 m). This test missile proved to be rugged, reliable and safe, and from it much useful data were obtained.

Other General Electric rocket vehicles were being designed during this period too. Missiles given the designation HERMES A2, A3, B and C1 were undergoing development programmes.[16] While all of these were not produced, lessons learned were incorporated in other

FIG. 7.3. *The HERMES missile followed the configuration of the German WASSERFALL but had a new propulsion system and method of guidance. This photograph shows the final stage of pre-flight checking before launching from White Sands Proving Ground.* (Photo. General Electric Company)

missile designs. The A2 programme was directed towards the design and development of a short-range guided missile but although the vehicle has been tested no further information has yet been released.

The HERMES B programme had as its ultimate objective the design of a supersonic ramjet missile and for this purpose two full-sized supersonic ramjet diffusers were mounted on the nose of V-2 rockets for flight testing. Work was also going on concerning the HERMES C1, a three-stage, long-range glider type of guided missile. Initial results of a study indicated that this glider type of missile would have a very long range, and a preliminary analysis was made of the weights, the dimensions, thrust, propulsion, motors and the control methods which would be needed and which was based on the information available at that time. These early projects were finally terminated while the General Electric Company concentrated its efforts on the development of other important missile systems.

The missiles flown by the General Electric Company since 1951 indeed resulted in many new contributions to missile guidance and propulsion systems. Research and development achievements of project HERMES included not only the first launching of a large rocket in the Western Hemisphere, but also the design, construction, and operation of the first static test facilities in the United States, development of an engine with the highest specific impulse ever achieved in rocket flight, and the first command control of a missile in flight in the United States. Two new guidance systems for surface-to-surface guided missiles were also developed. During 1954 the General Electric Company tested in flight a new and considerably advanced guided missile, and has conducted research in high performance propellants and propulsion system refinements.

In a speech to the United States Air Force Institute of Technology[17] the Assistant Secretary of the Air Force, Trevor Gardner, said that fighter bomber forces have become somewhat handicapped in their ability to operate in darkness and in bad weather, and that to offset this deficiency the Air Force had chosen a tactical guided missile, the MATADOR. This missile can be used in day or night operations, during all weathers, and can be operated from dispersed positions in the face of enemy air superiority. In fact operational units have been organized and deployed to Europe and the Far East. He also confirmed that the Air Force had been developing missiles to increase the long-range striking power, to assist the Strategic Air Command, and that three intercontinental missiles were at that date under accelerated development. These missiles are the North American NAVAHO, the Northrop SNARK and the Convair ATLAS. It was claimed that each of these missiles has an intercontinental atomic capability but that they have differing overall performances. As far as the United States Navy is concerned, Rear-Admiral John H. Sides[18] revealed during a Secretary of Defence Symposium in New York on the 1st December 1954 that the REGULUS, a recoverable guided missile that can be flown repeatedly, had been fired not only from an attack carrier but also from a submarine, the USS *Tunny*. The REGULUS in its training version can be recovered after a target run. This is an important feature achieved by the use of retractable landing gear and a parabrake, and has enabled several flights to be made with a single missile. The United States Army has the CORPORAL and the HONEST JOHN. The former follows a ballistic trajectory in its flight to the target and it is essentially an improved V-2 type of rocket. HONEST JOHN, on the other hand, is an artillery rocket which is unguided.

Dealing first with the modern tactical weapons, the specifications for the Martin MATADOR were laid down in 1946[19] and these called for a medium range, surface-to-surface missile. At an early stage it was realized that the choice of a launching system could be one of the most difficult phases of missile development, and finally a zero-length launching arrangement was chosen because of its tactical superiority. In 1947 the Glenn L. Martin Company built ten dynamically similar, full-scale, wooden flight dummies of the MATADOR (a small swept-wing aircraft with a T-tail), and one launching platform to prove the theory of the zero-length launch. The assisted take-off rocket used for launching was a 40,000 to 45,000 lb (18 to 20,400 kg) thrust, 2-sec duration, Aerojet unit. The design called for having the thrust axis of the rocket passing through the missile's centre of gravity. After several successful flights intentional misalignments of the rocket axis were made to determine the permissible off-tolerances.

The first seven model firings established the engineering validity of both missile configuration and the launching arrangement. Five flights were made at Aberdeen Proving Grounds and two at the Martin Airport in Maryland. At the same time the Glenn L. Martin

Company built fifteen experimental versions so that the missile could be flight tested as a whole. These experimental missiles were flown at Holloman Air Force Base in 1949 and 1950. It was during this period, too, that the guidance system was being developed, and the Glenn L. Martin Company, in common with other companies in the missile field, established their own electronic section. Service flights with the final missile were begun at Holloman in 1950 and were continued at Patrick Air Force Base in 1951 and 1952, with

the result that the missile was proved ready to go into full-scale production.

The first flight of a production model was in November 1952, less than one year after the complete engineering release in December

FIG. 7.4. *A series of photographs showing the launching of the tactical surface-to-surface MATADOR missile from Cape Canaveral, Florida. The way in which the launching device swings forward to avoid fouling the booster and the booster separation are clearly illustrated.*

(Photos. U.S. Information Service)

1951. It was not, however, until 1954, after a number of training programmes had been completed, that the United States Air Force announced that the MATADOR would be deployed in the field. The length of the MATADOR is 39·6 ft (12 m) and its body diameter 54 in (137 cm). The wing span is 28·7 ft (8·75 m). Propulsion is by an Allison J-33-A-37 turbo-jet which gives the missile a speed of over 650 m.p.h. (1,000 km/hr) and a ceiling of over 35,000 ft (10,500 m).

This missile was the first tactical unmanned weapon of the United States Air Force and forms the basis of a number of pilotless bomber squadrons, several of which are stationed in Europe and in the Far East. The launcher can be quickly towed from one place to another thereby overcoming the vulnerability of the old V-1 launching sites. Both the launcher and the missile can be easily shipped in transport aircraft such as the Douglas C 124 Globemaster, so that pilotless bomber squadrons can be rapidly located whenever they may be needed. The MATADOR cruises at Mach 0·9 and is accordingly difficult to intercept by aircraft. Defence against it would probably best be obtained by ground-to-air missiles. The launching weight is 12,000 lb (5,400 kg) and its range approximately 600 miles (960 km).

The launching of MATADOR from the zero-length launcher is made at an angle of 15 deg. The front end of the missile is supported by two ball and sockets, whereas the rear is supported by a bolt. The MATADOR jet engine is started and brought up to full thrust and then the rocket assisted take-off unit is fired. The combined thrust of the jet engine and the solid-propellant rocket is sufficient to shear the rear retaining bolt. The missile moves forward, swinging away from the front supports which drop away and allow clearance for the booster motor. (*Fig.* 7.4.)

The Chance Vought REGULUS is a similar type of winged missile used by the United States Navy. It was developed under the sponsorship of the Navy Bureau of Aeronautics and has increased tremendously the striking power of the surface and submarine forces. It was designed for launching from submarines, surface ships, or shore bases, and it is now in full-scale production. REGULUS can deliver a powerful warhead at transonic speeds over a range of hundreds of miles, guided along its course by a built-in electronic brain.

The REGULUS was conceived by Chance Vought in 1947.[20] Its existence was not released until March 1953 when the Navy announced that the programme had reached a stage where information concerning some of its earlier phases could be released to give the public information concerning engineering and technical progress made by the Navy department and its contractors in the field of missiles. First flight of a test vehicle was made in 1950 from Edwards Air Force Base. (*Fig. 7.5.*)

FIG. 7.5 *A tactical surface-to-surface winged missile used by the U.S. Navy is the Chance Vought REGULUS shown here being launched by means of two solid-propellant booster rockets. The REGULUS can be launched from ships or from shore bases.* (Photo. Chance Vought Aircraft/U.S. Navy)

In addition to contracting for a tactical missile, the Navy had instructed an exceptional requirement, the basic missile configuration must contain provision for recovery. This meant that the missile, in its test and training versions, must be capable of landing intact after a mission so that it could be flown again. REGULUS was hence designed in two versions; a recoverable test and training missile with a retractable landing gear, and a non-recoverable tactical missile. In practice REGULUS missiles have been flown as many as ten times and one missile has flown fifteen times.

REGULUS is a swept-wing, tailless aircraft powered by a turbo-jet. It is boosted at take-off by a pair of solid-propellant rocket boosters. Pitch control is obtained from moveable surfaces inborne on the wings, roll control from ailerons mounted nearer to the tips. REGULUS is about 30 ft (9·1 m) in length. The training version of the REGULUS is equipped with drone type of guidance, but when used as a tactical missile it has its own long-range guidance system. Its range is indeed about 200 miles (320 km).

The Ryan FIREBEE is also now produced in a version which can be used as a tactical ground-to-ground missile. (*Fig.* 7.6.) The maximum speed of the missile is 610 m.p.h. (1,000 km/hr) and its range is just over 650 miles (1,090 km). The ceiling is about 40,000 ft (12,000 m) and the length of the missile is 17 ft 3 in (5·26 m). It is equipped with swept wings having a span of 11 ft 2 in (3·5 m), and the empty weight is 1,180 lb (535 kg), the full weight being 1,845 lb (836 kg). It can carry a warhead of about 500 lb (227 kg) and it is propelled by a Continental-Marbore turbo-jet or a Fairchild Ranger turbo-jet.

FIG. 7.6. *FIREBEE was originally a target drone but has now been modified as a tactical missile. It can be surface or air launched and is powered by a turbo-jet engine, the Fairchild J-44.*

(Photo. U.S. Air Force)

The great disadvantage of this class of winged tactical missile is that they are vulnerable to interception by air-to-air or ground-to-air missiles. If the attacker is to be assured of success he must use much faster vehicles to carry his explosive warhead. The answer is, of course, the long-range ballistic missile which is extremely difficult if not impossible to intercept.

In this second class of vehicles there is the Douglas HONEST JOHN which is a heavy field artillery rocket. It is notable for its good mobility compared with equal calibre normal artillery. The missile, which is about 26 ft (8 m) in length, has a maximum diameter of 30 in (76 cm) and a take-off weight of 6,000 lb (2,700 kg). It is fired from a special combined transporter and launcher. Propulsion is by means of a solid-propellant rocket unit, so that the missile is essentially an unguided rocket which can carry atomic or high explosive warheads over a range of from 20 to 25 miles (30 to 40 km). Aiming is very much like that of a gun and the rocket then travels at supersonic speed along a ballistic trajectory to its target. This missile is produced by Douglas Aircraft for Army Ordnance and it is claimed to pack a greater punch and to have a higher mobility than conventional ordnance.

In-flight stability is obtained by small rockets mounted in blisters behind the warhead and which produce spinning of the missile. HONEST JOHN was first test fired at White Sands in 1951 and production began in 1953. An advanced version with much longer range is being developed.

The CORPORAL is a much larger missile. (*Fig.* 7.7.) It was developed from the Caltech experiments and is produced by the Firestone Tyre and Rubber Company, with Gillfillan Brothers making the radio guidance equipment. Propulsion is by a liquid-propellant rocket engine produced by the Ryan Aeronautical Company, and the missile has an overall length of 40 ft (12·2 m) and a maximum diameter of 30 in (76 cm). Exhaust vanes are used as in the V-2 to control the direction of thrust of the motor and to establish the missile on its correct ballistic trajectory which can carry it some 100 miles (160 km) to its target. Atomic or conventional warheads can be carried.

A mobile launcher comprises both transport and launching device. The missile is transported in a horizontal position and then a hydraulic erector and winch raises it to the vertical position, for it to be placed on a four-armed cradle above a conical flame deflector.

FIG. 7.7. *The CORPORAL rocket is a ballistic tactical missile which is powered by a liquid-propellant rocket engine and can carry an atomic or high explosive warhead. Batteries of these rockets are now being deployed in Europe.*

(Photo. Ryan Aeronautical Co.)

The erecting arm is then lowered, and the missile is ready for launching. Pre-launching servicing is carried out from a mobile working platform which is mounted on the end of a long hinged arm which can be easily transported on a truck.

The CORPORAL seems to follow current practice as with the VIKING and certain British missiles, of making tanks integral with the skin and channelling the control wires and feed lines in conduits running along the outside of these tanks. This was a feature of the WAC CORPORAL, an earlier rocket of the series which led to the CORPORAL.

The take-off weight of the rocket is 12,000 lb (5,440 kg) and it reaches a speed of Mach 3 at all-burnt. The battery equipped with these missiles consists of ten transporters and ten launching tables and needs just over 500 men for its operation.

The United States Army contend that the weapon gives the field commander a far greater fire power on the battlefield than is obtainable from conventional weapons—presumably meaning support aircraft, for other weapons would not have a comparable range— and enables him to strike deep into enemy defences with atomic or high explosive warheads. CORPORAL rockets are being made available to the Commonwealth Army as part of the technical exchanges concerning missiles which were negotiated by Mr. Duncan Sandys during the summer of 1954. In fact some CORPORAL batteries are now being deployed in Europe. The CORPORAL rocket guidance system maintains the rocket on the axis of a radar beam until burnout. After this it follows a ballistic trajectory.

NATIV was an early ground-to-ground test missile developed by the North American Aviation Company using a bi-propellant rocket motor to attain supersonic speed, it had a ceiling of 55,000 ft (16,800 m) which would indicate a range of 20 miles (30 km). Take-off weight was 1,240 lb (562 kg), overall length 14·5 ft (4·42 m), maximum diameter 18 in (45·7 cm), and launching was from a special tower. The North American Aviation Company produces a range of rocket motors, some having multiple cylinders and very large thrusts which are used extensively in American missiles. The development of a further long-range missile was indicated by three experimental ascents made by a vehicle known as Convair MX 774 (*Fig.* 7.8), a research rocket which attained altitudes of more than 100 miles (160 km) and was designed similar to the V-2 rockets.

Of the three strategic intercontinental missiles which are under accelerated development in the United States the NAVAHO has passed its initial flight test and is supposed to have a range of at least 4,000 miles (6,500 km). It is launched by a rocket boost and climbs to an altitude exceeding 50,000 ft (15,000 m). Propulsion is then continued on two ramjets and the ceiling is reported to be about 100,000 ft (30,000 m). The top speed is about Mach 2·5, but this is exceeded as the NAVAHO dives towards its target, when its velocity may reach four times that of sound.

The SNARK is a long-range winged missile powered by a turbo-jet. It is another swept winged pilotless bomber this time produced by Northrop. It probably has a range of 4,000 miles (6,500 km). SNARK was originally powered by an Allison J 71 turbo-jet but now uses a Pratt and Whitney J 57 turbo-jet. It uses a solid-propellant boosted

Fig. 7.8. *An early test vehicle in the series which has led to the ATLAS intercontinental ballistic missile was the Convair MX-774. This missile was powered by a liquid oxygen/alcohol, four-cylinder rocket engine developed by reaction motors and giving a thrust of 8,000 lb.*

(Photo. Reaction Motors Inc.)

rocket take-off from a zero-length launcher. Snark cruises nearly at the speed of sound and is guided by a star tracking inertial system. The turbo-jet engine gives 10,000 lb (4,500 kg) of thrust and the cruising altitude is just over 40,000 ft (12,000 m). The missile has a swept vertical tail, is 32 ft (9·2 m) long, and has wings of 40 ft (12·2 m) span. Preliminary tests have been completed and it is now reported that flight tests have moved to Cocoa Florida where extensions of the long-range proving grounds have been arranged with the British Government, and one vehicle flew 2,000 miles into the Atlantic.

But the most formidable weapon is, of course, the ballistic vehicle especially when this can be employed over intercontinental ranges. It is[21] claimed that the ATLAS is launched by 'rocket motors developing thousands of tons of thrust and millions of horsepower within seconds' and that the rocket would travel at speeds of several thousands of miles per hour. The employment of such missiles it is contended would present any enemy with an incredibly—almost hopelessly—difficult defensive task, though ionization of the atmosphere at the re-entry speed of over Mach 7 would provide one means of detection. ATLAS has a burning time of the order of 12 min and an all-burnt velocity of 22,000 ft per sec (6,700 m/sec). The peak trajectory altitude will be in the region of 800 miles (1,300 km) and the time of flight to a target 5,000 miles (8,000 km) distance will be only 30 min. It uses a liquid-propellant rocket engine for the first stage which has been developed by the North American Aviation and gives a thrust of 120,000 lb (54,500 kg). (*Fig. 7.9.*) It will be able to land within a 10-mile radius of its target.

A second American intercontinental ballistic missile is to be developed by the Glenn L. Martin Company under the designation of WS 107 TITAN. Indeed it is reported that the United States will budget for £200 million guided weapon expenses in 1957.

In France there is the VERONIQUE. The VERONIQUE is a high altitude research vehicle and reaches a speed of just over 3,000 m.p.h. (4,800 km/hr) and consequently has a range comparable with the V-2, but it is a fairly small rocket being only 1 ft 9 in (0·55 m) in diameter and 19 ft 9 in (6 m) in length. The take-off weight is about 1 ton and the rocket motor develops a thrust of 4 tons for a period of 35 sec. Altitudes in the 100 miles (160 km) level have been obtained during tests at the Sahara Rocket Proving Grounds. There is also a rocket-boosted ramjet, the SE 4200, which has a range of about 70 miles (190 km).

A development from the V-2 is the REDSTONE which arises from the work of the Redstone Arsenal group where many ex-Peenemünde German scientists are working, and this missile is to be produced by Chrysler. It is a rocket which is larger than the V-2 and it uses a 75,000 lb thrust bi-propellant rocket unit constructed by North American Aviation. The REDSTONE is used by the United States Army as a medium-range weapon and has a range of about 300 miles (500 km). It is controlled by jet and air vanes and was first test fired in 1953 after ten years of development.

FIG. 7.9. *It is understood that the ATLAS first stage will be powered by a large liquid propellant rocket engine manufactured by North American Aviation. A typical rocket power plant manufactured by that company is shown being static tested in the mountains near to Los Angeles. Motors like this develop thousands of pounds of thrust.*

(Photo. North American Aviation Inc.)

First tests with multi-stage vehicles for long-range bombardment were made in the HERMES Programme of the General Electric Company, namely the Bumper series of experiments. During these experiments a number of missiles, which each consisted of a V-2 rocket with a WAC CORPORAL as its payload, were fired, some from White Sands, and some from the long-range proving grounds at Patrick Air Force Base, in Florida. The small second stage was ignited at the completion of the burning period of the V-2 and it reached a final velocity of Mach 7 and a record altitude, on 24th February 1949, of 242 miles (387 km). Eight BUMPER WACs in all were launched,[22] six from White Sands and two from Florida. The missiles launched from New Mexico had altitude as their objective, while those from Patrick AFB were placed into horizontal trajectories in order to obtain data concerning aerodynamic heating and drag at high velocities. The main problems overcome by the Bumper Programme were those associated with the effective separation of the stages as close as possible to the time of burn-out of the first stage, and the starting of the rocket motor of the second stage at extreme altitudes. One factor which was known to become important with high trajectory vehicles is the rotation of the Earth. The Coriolis acceleration caused a displacement of the impact point about 15 miles (24 km) to the west of where it would have been in the case of a non-rotating Earth, and this had to be corrected by arranging that the line of take-off should be rotated 10 deg to the east. Another important result from the tests was that it was shown feasible for two-way communication to take place with the second stage moving above the D, E, and F ionized layers of the upper atmosphere.

Project Bumper, indeed, proved that step vehicles were practical, and its realization has led to the development not only of the intercontinental ballistic missile but also of the Earth satellite vehicle.

Besides the vehicles which have been developed purely for military purposes there are a number of rockets which have been used in high-altitude research programmes and on which a fairly large amount of data have been forthcoming. These rockets are very important because from the data released it is possible to say that the military art has indeed progressed so far, and it can be postulated that it is now beyond the stage as exemplified by these rockets. We know too that if a rocket has an altitude of a certain figure then its range can be double that figure. The Bumper-WAC, for example, the second stage of which reached nearly 250 miles (400 km), could if fired as a ballistic missile have a range of 500 miles (800 km). In the United States there is the AEROBEE which is a two-stage rocket consisting of a solid-propellant booster and a liquid-propellant second stage, and there are reports of advanced versions of this, known as the AEROBEE-HI, reaching altitudes of 160 miles (260 km). A ground-to-ground missile based on the AEROBEE could therefore have a range of 300 miles (480 km) and could probably carry a small atomic warhead. In America, too, there is the large VIKING rocket which has reached 158 miles (256 km) as a single-stage rocket. If the VIKING (*Fig.* 7.10) were made the second stage of a much larger rocket then it is possible to see why intercontinental ranges become quite feasible.

Modern analyses have shown that it can take between two or three hours for a deterrent atomic bomber to be placed into the air following the receipt of an early warning, while the radar warnings available—even in respect of conventional atomic bomber attack—will be only between fifteen and thirty minutes. Obviously early attacks will be made against strategic air fields and it would appear, therefore, that a British atom bomber deterrent is cancelled from the word go. In addition to guided weapon defence it would appear that Britain must also have a guided weapon deterrent force if she is to remain a military power.

The case of the United States of America is very different, as adequate warning can be given to the strategic bomber bases inland so that the bombers can be airborne long before the bases can be bombed by conventional transonic atom bombers.

As advocated immediately after the last war[23] Britain must concentrate technical effort on long-range guided weapons or fade into military insignificance. It is of little use to have developed a thermonuclear weapon if the means of delivering it—airfields and the bombers—are destroyed before they can be used. Missile sites are much less vulnerable than airfields, and suitable choice of propellants should make it possible for strategic missiles to be launched much more quickly than strategic bombers can become airborne.

Although it took several hours to prepare a V-2 for launching it has to be remembered that the V-2 was a mobile tactical vehicle. Intercontinental weapons could be readied in camouflaged launching bases which can be concealed more easily than airfields, and if they are designed as retaliation weapons they can use a choice of propellants which will make it possible for them to be loaded with the propellants and stored ready for firing almost at instant notice.

FIG. 7.10. *Releases on high altitude research vehicles such as the Glenn L. Martin VIKING rocket shown here give an indication of how the military art is developing. It is reasonable to assume that military vehicles are better than the declassified projects.*

(Photo. Glenn L. Martin Co.)

TABLE 7.1   *A-Series of Missiles*

Designa-tion	Year	Weight lb	Weight kg	Thrust lb	Thrust kg	Notes
A-1	1933	330	150	660	300	None fired
A-2	1934	330	150	660	300	First launching
A-3	1938	1,640	750	3,300	1,500	Subsonic
A-4	1940	27,500	12,500	55,000	25,000	Operational V-2
A-5	1938	1,640	750	3,300	1,500	A-4 prototype
A-6	—	—	—	—	—	Design study only
A-7	1941	1,750	800	3,300	1,500	A-5 with wings
A-9	1945	28,500	13,000	55,000	25,000	A-4 with wings
A-10	1945	191,000	87,000	440,000	200,000	Design study for A-9 booster

TABLE 7.2   *High-Altitude Research Vehicles*

Name	Manufac-turer	Propulsion	Weights Launching lb kg	Dry lb kg	Peak Altitude miles km
V-2	Peene-münde	Peene-münde	27,500 12,500	8,690 3,900	133 213
Viking	Martin	Reaction Motors	16,800 7,620	3,360 1,530	158 253
Bumper-WAC	General Electric	German and Aero-jet	28,000 12,700	8,690 3,900	242 387
WAC-Corporal	Douglas	Aerojet	665 300	300 136	45 72
Aerobee	Douglas	Aerojet	1,100 500	940 425	100 160
Veronique	LRBA Vernon	LRBA	2,240 1.000	920 420	90 144
Deacon	Alleghany Ballistics Lab.	A.B.L.	200 90	30* 13·6	60 96

The WAC-Corporal and Aerobee are tower launched by means of a solid-propellant booster. The Deacon is launched at high altitudes from a balloon.

* Refers to the payload weight.

LRBA means the Laboratoires Recherches Ballistique et Aeronautique. The Aerobee now appears in a modified Aerobee-Hi which is attaining altitudes of 150 miles (240 km).

TABLE 7.3

Name and manufacturer	Status	Designation	Propulsion	Guidance	Overall length		Ceiling		Range		Launching weights (ton)
					ft	*m*	*miles*	*km*	*miles*	*km*	
FZG.76 (V-1)	Operational	WTM	Pulse-jet	Pre-set	25	7·6	3	5	190	300	2
A.4 (V-2)	Operational	BTM	L.P.R.	Inertial	47	14·4	N/A	N/A	200	320	12·7
Matador, Martin	Production	WTM	Turbo-jet SP.R.	Radio and inertial	40	12·2	?	?	600	1,000	5
Regulus, Chance Vought	Production	WTM	Turbo-jet SP.R.	Radio and Inertial	30	9·1	?	?	300?	500?	6·5
Snark, Northrop	Development	WSM	Turbo-jet R.B	Celestial	32	9·2	8	13	4,000	6,400	?
Navaho, North American	Development	WSM	Ramjet L.P.R.B	Celestial	?	?	18	30	5,000	8,000	?
Honest John, Douglas	Production	BTM	SP.R	None	26	7·9	N/A	N/A	25	40	2·75
Corporal, Firestone	Production	BTM	L.P.R	Beam rider	40	12·2	N/A	N/A	125	200	5
Hermes A.1, General Electric	Test vehicle	BTM	L.P.R	—	25·5	7·8	N/A	N/A	50	80	3·5
Hermes A.2, General Electric	Test vehicle	BTM	L.P.R	—	?	?	N/A	N/A	300	480	11
Hermes B, General Electric	Design study	BTM	Ramjet	—	?	?	N/A	N/A	?	?	?
Hermes C, General Electric	Design study	WSM	L.P.R	—	?	?	N/A	N/A	2,000	3,200	?
Redstone, Chrysler	Production	BTM	L.P.R	Inertial	50	15	N/A	N/A	300	500	15
Atlas, Convair	Development	BSM	L.P.R	Inertial	100	30	N/A	N/A	5,000	8,000	70
Soviet, A.4	Production	BTM	L.P.R	Inertial	45	13·8	N/A	N/A	500	800	12·5
Soviet, 2-stage	Production	BSM	L.P.R	Inertial	60?	18·3	N/A	N/A	2,000	3,200	50
British, English Electric	Development	BSM	L.P.R	Celestial?	?	?	N/A	N/A	1,500	2,400	?

REFERENCES

[1] BURGESS, E., *Aircraft*, **33**, 6, March 1955.

[2] SUTTON, G. P., *Jnl. British Inter. Soc.*, **13**, 5, Sept. 1954, 262–8.

[3] BURGESS, E., *World Science Review*, Dec. 1955, 3–10.

[4] KOOY, J. M. J., UYTENBOGAART, J. W. H., *Ballistics of the Future*, H. Stam, Haarlem, Ch. X.

[5] BURGESS, E., *The Engineer*, **184**, 31 Oct. 1947, 408–9.

[6] GATLAND, K. W. G., *Jnl. British Inter. Soc.*, **7**, 4, July 1948, 160–9.

[7] BURGESS, E., loc. cit., 5.

[8] *Jnl. British Inter. Soc.*, **7**, 2, March 1948, 92.

[9] DORNBERGER, W. R., *Jnl. British Inter Soc.*, **13**, 5, Sep. 1954, 245–62.

[10] PERRING, W. G. A., *Jnl. Royal Aero. Soc.*, **50**, 1946, 483.

[11] KOOY, J. M. J., UYTENBOGAART, J. W. H., loc. cit., 4, Ch. XI.

[12] GENERAL ELECTRIC COMPANY, *News Bureau Release*, Dec. 1954.

[13] HAVILAND, R. P., *Jnl. British Inter. Soc.*, **11**, 2, Jan. 1952, 9–13.

[14] BURGESS, E., *Frontier to Space*, Chapman & Hall Ltd., London, 1955, Macmillan Co., New York, 1956, *Raketen in der Ionospharenforschung*, Deutsche Radar Verlag. Garmisch-Partenkirchen, 1956.

[15] ANON., *General Electric Review*, **57**, 2, Mar. 1954, 8–22.

[16] GENERAL ELECTRIC, *Missile Memo*, R55AO519, 1955.

[17] GARDNER, T., *USAF Release*, 15 Mar. 1955.

[18] SIDES, J. H., *Sperryscope*, **13**, 9, 1955, 2–7.

[19] GLENN L. MARTIN CO., *Press Releases*, 11554, 21455, 1951.

[20] CHANCE VOUGHT AIRCRAFT, *Press Release*, 1954.

[21] GARDNER, T., loc. cit., 17.

[22] HAVILAND, R. P., loc. cit., 13.

[23] BURGESS, E., *R.A.F. Quarterly*, **17**, 3, June 1946, 153–9.

CHAPTER VIII

PRODUCTION AND DEVELOPMENT

◎

AT THE END of World War II there were a number of guided missiles in advanced stages of development. Moreover many of the fundamental guidance systems had been proposed. One may wonder then why ten years later most of the nations are still without a really adequate guided weapon defensive system as protection even against conventional bombers.

Essentially the problem has been that of achieving reliability in weapon systems. Some missile systems have operated quite satisfactorily when they have been under the control of the scientists and technicians who have designed and constructed prototype test vehicles. But this does not mean that the system would still function efficiently in operations when it has to be serviced and the missile fired by members of the Armed Forces who must necessarily be not as highly specialized in missile technology as those scientists who made the missile in the first instance. Similarly, guidance systems which may look superlative on paper and, indeed, may operate successfully under peacetime conditions, may often be susceptible to new enemy jamming devices. The designers of missile guidance systems, therefore, have at all times to try to be one step ahead of jamming techniques. This needs a close tie up with military scientific intelligence as well as keeping to the forefront in routine technological developments of electronics.

Missiles must be 100 per cent reliable. This high degree of reliability is called for because the missile is a pilotless vehicle and there is no human mind to exercise judgement and to correct for minor errors or malfunctions which could quite easily develop from mechanical or electronic breakdown during a flight. As has been pointed out earlier the development of missiles is very different from that of conventional aircraft where one or two experimental prototypes can be flown many times and can be modified as the tests proceed. The missile on the contrary must be regarded as expendable, except in certain modern investigations where attempts are made to recover the missile by parachute at the end of the test. Nevertheless, a successful missile may require as many as 100 prototypes before it can be developed to a stage where it is ready for production, and although it would be quite easy to tool up a production line to produce 100 missiles, this cannot be done for the test vehicles because each one of them will be quite different from its predecessor.

At no stage in missile development must performance be increased by a sacrifice in reliability. It has, indeed, been suggested[1] that until a fundamental approach to the engineering problem of reliability is made guided missile development must depend upon the method of successive approximations which can produce results of reasonable reliability. An important point arising from the V-2 firings by the General Electric Company was that simplicity of missile design pays dividends. A guided missile can, indeed, usually be regarded as a system of components in series. If one of these components fails, the missile itself will fail. The reliability of the complete missile cannot be better than that of its weakest component. For example, if there are several hundred components in a missile, each having a reliability of, say, 99 per cent, the effect is that the complete missile will only be 5 per cent reliable. This figure is by no means acceptable; but finding out why missiles fail is a colossal task, and also an expensive one. In the case of the V-2 failures encountered during the series of firings in the United States, thirty out of thirty-six cases were caused by unknown factors which were never identified.[2] The more complex a missile becomes, the more time does it take to eliminate the possibility of failure. It appears that only by duplication of components that are likely to fail—with a consequent sacrifice of good mass ratios and accordingly of range—can missiles be made as reliable as aircraft where duplication is an established practice.

The problem has been that of starting with the experimental control mechanisms which have been constructed in the guided missile laboratories, and having to redesign and to make them suitable for mass production using printed circuits, transistors, and the minimum of expensive tooling. In addition they had to be made capable of swift and easy checking by service personnel on a 'pass' or 'reject' basis. This is most essential because in the event of any emergency the skilled personnel required for the maintenance of complex electronic devices will be in extremely short supply, and modern ideas of war do not include the possibility of having time to train new personnel for the operation of weapons. Even to-day the armed services are finding it extremely difficult to attract the right quantity of technicians to maintain the complex devices associated with normal aircraft.

Another great time-consuming factor in the development of missiles has been in the difficulty of testing them against the type of target they will be expected to meet in battle. Drones have been used to simulate bombers. (*Fig.* 8.1.) Sometimes, in order to save the loss arising from destruction of these drones, which in themselves are quite expensive guided missiles, the warhead of the test missile ejects a marking powder instead of exploding lethally.

FIG. 8.1. *Missiles have to be tested against the type of target they will be expected to meet operationally. Drones are used for this purpose. One example is the JINDIVIK jet-propelled aircraft. For take-off a launching trolley is used and the drone can be recovered by landing on a skid.*

(Photo. L.R.W.E. Salisbury/Armstrong Siddeley)

Missiles are, moreover, fantastically complex. The NIKE system, for example, has more than $1\frac{1}{2}$ million separate parts. It has been found also that missiles appear to have most of the problems associated with the development of aircraft and quite a number of additional special peculiarities. Experiences show that missiles take up less time in the actual design stage on the drawing board than do aircraft but that they need more analytical work. (*Fig.* 8.2.)

In order that the highly complex missile components can be tested quickly in the field before firing by less skilled personnel, a number of items of equipment have now been designed. One example is the Solartron servo test set which can be used by semi-skilled personnel to check the servomechanisms at four spot frequencies. Two centre-zero meters give a quick 'pass' or 'reject' indication so that the operator has only to connect the equipment and switch the four spot

FIG. 8.2. *In order to speed the development of a guided missile and minimize actual live firings, the analytical work is done by means of computers and simulators. At Bell Telephone Laboratories equipment was built to study the action of NIKE by means of an electro-mechanical simulator which represented the NIKE missile.* (Photo. Bell Telephone Laboratories)

frequencies previously chosen while noting that neither meter passes into the reject part of its scale. Another example arises because automatic tracking and homing radar cannot be calibrated on fixed targets. Simulators have been designed to test units for target attenuation, and motion of single or multiple type targets, for various radar pulse repetition rates, for various pulse widths and aerial beam patterns.[3]

The guided weapon programme also requires the training of personnel in the operation of radar devices for the long-range detection of missiles, aircraft, and pilotless bombers. Radar simulators become an essential part of the defensive training weapon system. One recently produced by Solartron known as the tactical radar simulator, uses a plan position indicator and a range height indicator on which any aircraft can be simulated over a wide range of performance values together with targets such as guided missiles and ballistic rockets. Tight formations of aircraft, interference, jamming, effects of window, wind drift, curvature of the Earth's surface, and tropospheric refraction, are all accounted for, so that personnel can be trained to a high peak of efficiency without the expense of a single missile being fired. This of course considerably reduces the running cost of any guided weapon training programme; a most important point because before missiles can pass into operational use sufficient numbers of personnel must be trained to service, arm, and fire them.

Missiles, too, have a large number of relays in their instrumentations; and relays are notoriously troublesome items of equipment. Especially is this so when it is remembered that a missile may have to be stored for several years and then it must have all its components operating faultlessly when fired. One calculation[4] shows that in a typical guided weapon installation one failure only in 10,000 of any of the relay links would mean that the complete vehicle could only be 85 per cent sure of firing correctly.

Even in the propulsive mechanism difficulties can be encountered. Rockets, for example, appear deceptively straightforward in design and, indeed, have been described as the simplest type of heat engine. In fact they are by no means simple; they need complex plumbing and control wiring. Every aspect of rocket design is critical and because of this critical nature the demands placed upon the manufacturers of rocket engines are extreme. (*Fig.* 8.8.) All the surfaces in the motor, the nozzle and the cooling passages, and all the valves and the plumbing must be fabricated with precision, while the materials used must be compatible with the propellants which are often highly corrosive and reactive liquids. Tiny imperfections in the lines and the valves or in the injectors can alter the propellant flow and cause violently unstable, or even destructive, combustion.

Guided missiles also must be designed to use readily available materials as much as possible. Castings rather than forgings are used to reduce production costs. An example of how special techniques for the construction of missiles were developed is in the aluminium honeycomb-slab wing construction of the Martin MATADOR. (*Fig.* 8.3.) The slabs are cut to shape by a semi-automatic high-speed band saw (*Fig.* 8.4) and the wing itself is made up by the core sections being metal bonded to each other and to the skin of

FIG. 8.3. *The wings and tail unit of the Martin MATADOR were formed from a honeycomb material by means of single tool shown in this photograph. This considerably reduces production time and costs.*

(Photo. Glenn L. Martin Co.)

FIG. 8.4. *The honeycomb core material for the wings of the MATADOR is cut to the correct shape by a single pass on the high-speed bandsaw shown in this photograph.*

(Photo. Glenn L. Martin Co.)

the wings. The wings are fabricated in two sections for ease in transportation and are assembled quickly and without difficulty by means of tension bolts. Essentially the MATADOR missile is designed so that it can be broken down into seven components to facilitate packing and shipping. Moreover, all these various sections are interchangeable so that if one becomes unserviceable a spare section can be used in its place.[5]

On the other hand a smaller missile like the FALCON is supplied in one single shipping crate for storage by the Air Force. In the case of the REGULUS it was found possible to save 30 per cent of the wing weight by the use of cast aluminium wing panels.

Packing and shipping of missiles is an important aspect of their production. Efforts to achieve reliability may be completely in vain unless the missile is protected during storage and transport. In the case of large missiles re-usable containers with suitable shock absorbing mountings for the missiles are preferable. Hermetic sealing is advisable to prevent corrosion and rust from atmospheric moisture.

The LARK missile contained an example of good design for electronic packaging.[6] Each stage of the electronic equipment was capable of being tested on the ground as it was installed in a closed container with only a single connexion for the wiring. Indeed connexions between each stage were made by single sockets in each quadrant in the body section of the missile. Should a section fail on the ground test it could be easily replaced.

So far costs of missiles are extremely high though new techniques will probably reduce these in the coming years. For example it has been stated[7] that the cost of a missile which may be £6,500, can be broken down into £2,600 for the guidance equipment and the balance for airframe, propulsion unit and warhead. Test vehicles which are needed before the model is put into production may cost nearly twice as much as the production version. Figures such as these apply of course only to the smaller type of air-to-air or ground-to-air missiles.

But the development of guided weapons is not just that of the production of the missiles themselves. These are quite useless without the early warning which must be given by an outflung chain of radar stations. Although the outer ring in Europe is decidedly patchy, especially to the north and south, the radar chain for the defence of the North American Continent is progressing very well. Millions of pounds are being spent in the far Northern territories of Canada on the borders of the Arctic in order to construct an additional chain of radar warning stations even farther north than the existing early warning line. This present chain known as the mid-Canada line extends across the Continent from east to west level with Hudson Bay, but the distant early warning line (DEW line), now being constructed, starts from Alaska and goes across to the Davis Straits and thence on into Thule in Greenland. Wings extend downward on either side in order to prevent any attack from coming along the edges and thus outflanking the defensive lines. Parts of these wings consist of off-shore radar stations which will be located from New York to Newfoundland 80 to 100 miles (130 to 160 km) at sea. Each station is supported by three legs 150 ft (45·7 m) in length and will stand on the continental shelf. At the present moment gaps in the defences are covered by large four-engined bomber type aircraft carrying the search radar installations and operating on a permanent patrol basis. It is only by the establishment of such extended radar warning stations that any measure of protection can be given even in times like today when push-button warfare is coming closer and closer. An example would be a ballistic missile having a 5,000 mile (8,000 km) range taking only 30 min from launching to the explosion of its nuclear warhead on the target. Unless early warning can be given there is absolutely nothing which can be done by the defences against such a missile. If a certain amount of early warning is possible it may be that the civilian populations could take shelter and also that a similar type of missile could be dispatched to explode a nuclear warhead in the path of the attacker.

The difficulty here is that such a defensive missile would have to be a fairly large multi-stage rocket, and it seems unlikely that it will be possible to hold such large rockets ready loaded with propellants for them to take off within 15 min of receiving a warning. Though as has been pointed out in the previous chapter this is an ideal which will have to be aimed for.

The limitation does not apply, of course, to the intercontinental ballistic missile itself because the attacker can choose the moment for the launching and arrange his fuelling and pre-flight checking programme accordingly.

Another important aspect of guided weapon development is the formidable task of preparing instruction and maintenance manuals. These have to give the fullest details of the weapon system so that the great complexity of even the simplest missiles calls for several hundred handbooks to fulfil this task.

The accent nowadays, therefore, appears to be that having developed anti-aircraft missiles which are capable of intercepting conventional types of aircraft moving at speeds below sonic velocity, early warning radar chains must be erected in strategic locations. Not only will the cities then have a possibility of defence by the ground-to-air missiles, but also modern supersonic fighters and supersonic interceptor type missiles for long ranges will have an opportunity of closing with the enemy raiders and dispatching air-to-air missiles well before the raiders reach the target area.

The next phase in the guided weapon development must be that of the production of more advanced anti-missile missiles, first to use against air-to-ground missiles and then more advanced vehicles to act as a defence against the intercontinental strategic missiles, both winged and ballistic. This matter is a tremendous problem and it is one that the defences are not likely to perfect for some years after the intercontinental weapons are themselves in production. Hence there is bound to be a period when the offensive weapons are well in advance of any defensive technique.

It is apparent that guided weapon developments must lead to vehicles moving at higher and higher velocities. This poses one of the greatest problems connected with guided weapon development; that is, the problem of finding suitable structural materials.

When bodies are moving at high speeds in the atmosphere, the air close to them is heated considerably so that next to the skin of the vehicle a high temperature boundary layer is formed. At twice the speed of sound, for example, the skin temperature due to the aerodynamic heating is 93° C, at three times the speed of sound the skin temperature has gone up to 400° C (*Fig.* 8.5), while at Mach 4 the temperature rises to over 800° C. Airframe designers must accordingly face the necessity of designing primary structures which can carry loads while they are hot.

This tremendous rise in temperature which starts beyond about Mach 2 gives rise to the popularly termed thermal barrier. There is a great difference, however, between the so-called sound barrier and this thermal barrier. In the former case the effect is transient; there is a rise in the drag coefficient which is maximum at about Mach 1, while having exceeded the speed of sound, conditions settle down again and the problems are largely overcome. The difficulties encountered in the case of the sound barrier are problems associated with accelerating the vehicle through the transonic region where aerodynamic conditions change so rapidly. In the case of the thermal barrier, however, there is no such amelioration of conditions with increasing speeds. In fact the temperatures continue to rise until fantastic values are obtained and the highest melting point materials fail.

The thermal barrier arises from the fact that surrounding the missile is a boundary layer of air which is relatively thin. It is in this boundary layer where the ambient atmosphere is accelerated to the speed of the missile. There are frictional forces existing between the various layers of air because of the differences in speeds between them, so that energy is transferred from the moving body to the surrounding air in the form of heat. In effect, the power plant instead of using the energy of the fuel to do work in moving the vehicle changes it to heat energy in this boundary layer. Accordingly the temperature of the boundary layer rises and the propulsive effects obtained from the engine are decreased at high velocities.

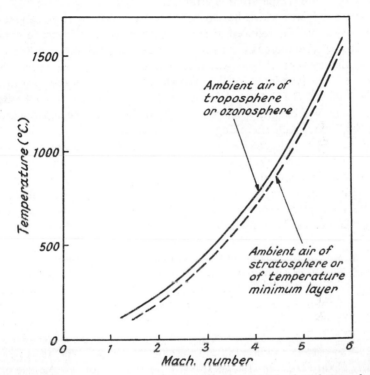

FIG. 8.5. *Skin temperature as a function of air speed. The dotted curve shows the effects when flying in the low temperature regions of the atmosphere, assuming that 90 per cent of the stagnation temperature is attained.*

One very important point is that the temperature rise is independent of the density of the atmosphere. It depends solely upon the relationship between the velocity of the missile and the velocity of sound in the atmosphere at the region considered. In point of fact flying higher in the atmosphere does improve conditions because the velocity of sound increases at high altitudes. Moreover, at high altitudes the ambient temperature of the atmosphere is much lower than at the surface and the air starts off from this lower temperature before it is heated. Even so in the temperature minimum regions, such as the stratosphere or the higher region at 300,000 ft (90,000 m), at Mach 4 the skin temperature can still rise to 800° C and to over 1,650° C at Mach 6. These figures assume that 90 per cent of the stagnation temperature is attained.

Another factor which has to be taken into consideration at great heights is that the reduced atmospheric density does improve conditions because there is not so much air per unit volume and, therefore, the amount of heat which it can pass back to the missile is reduced. The heat input into the vehicle falls with increasing altitude.

At 120,000 ft (33,500 m) for a missile travelling at Mach 4, the heat input will be only 1 per cent of that which would be experienced by the same missile travelling at Mach 4 at sea level.[8]

These high temperatures, of course, demand that newer types of structure and skin materials than those used in conventional aircraft shall be available.

With common airframe materials the specific strength falls off rapidly when temperatures increase beyond 90° C and these materials could not be used for most supersonic missiles. Many of the missiles which are to-day in production, however, are still only moving just above supersonic speed and consequently they use fairly conventional constructional materials. However, to-morrow's weapons— intercontinental ballistic missiles and anti-missile devices—will need new materials if they are to succeed in their tasks.

There are two ways of attacking the problem, one is to use new materials which can withstand the elevated skin temperatures, while the other is to use some kind of internal refrigeration. As far as new materials are concerned suggestions have been made for the use of titanium and various types of glass-laminated plastics. With refrigeration it is found that at speeds beyond Mach 3 the refrigeration capacity needed to keep the skin cool may end up by being something larger than the propulsion unit itself.

Heat is indeed a very great problem. Without some kind of preventative measures the interior of the missile would become unbearably hot. Most mechanisms and electrical apparatus are giving off heat which adds to that which is coming from the boundary layer, especially is this so because the mechanisms are crowded together in the vehicle. Use of sub-miniature packaging, which although it produces small sizes of components, still gives the same problems of heat dissipation. In the chapter concerning instrumentation it was pointed out that very often components are over-loaded because they are only operating for a short time, and again this results in the generation of more heat. In high-speed missiles temperatures will reach values at which ordinary solder would melt and silver solder has to be used. For insulation purposes extensive use must be made of silicones, fibreglass and ceramics. This is especially the case in missiles which have to travel for long periods of time at high speeds. Short-duration missiles, for example, ground-to-air, do not suffer these problems to the same extent as in, say, a long-range inter-continental missile which may have to travel at Mach 5 for a period of up to one hour before it reaches its target.

Internal refrigeration cannot rely upon the outside air as a coolant because the mere gathering of this air causes ram compression and adiabatic heating. In some missiles, therefore, the mass of the propellants is used as a heat sink for the refrigeration system. Yet another method is to evaporate a liquid carried within the missile itself, but this means reduced payloads; a reduction in the warhead weight which can be carried. Fortunately the problem of high temperatures can be met by material research. The modern gas turbine demanded higher temperatures than had previously been met with in the other types of heat engines. Materials were synthesized to meet the challenge of these increased temperatures. The same will take place in missile technology.

Three things are called for when considering the suitability of materials for high temperature applications. First is resistance to oxidation which is governed by the type of oxide film which is formed, for example, if it appears as a protective layer which will resist further oxidation. Secondly, high-temperature strength is needed. At low temperatures engineers make use of yield or tensile strength for designing structures but at elevated temperatures these become very different because the metal continues to deform as though it were plastic. This is known as creep.[9] Three stages occur, first a rapid elongation at a decreasing rate, then a constant rate, finally a rapidly increasing rate of extension leading to a complete failure of the material. At high temperatures it is thus found that metals possess both elastic and plastic properties simultaneously.

Finally, metals must resist corrosion. To do this it is usual to alloy the metal with chromium and nickel.

Alloys of metal which are temperature resistant can be classified into four main groups, the first of which includes the chrome nickel steels which are known as Austenitic steels. They are resistant to both oxidation and corrosion. Secondly steels which are martensitic or ferritic in crystalline structure contain chromium without nickel, and it is found that corrosion resistance is a function of the amount of chromium which is in the alloy. For very high temperatures as much as 30 per cent of chromium is required. Then nickel-base alloys, such as Inconel, contain between 70 to 80 per cent of nickel and they have very good creep resistance.

Cobalt based alloys are sometimes called 'super' alloys but as these use scarce materials like tungsten and cobalt as well as nickel and chromium they are expensive and can be only used in critical applications.[10]

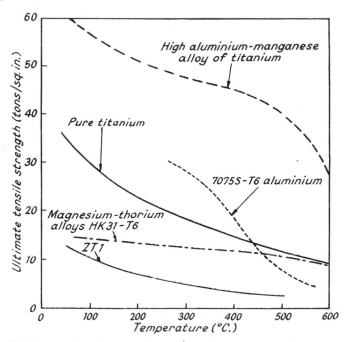

FIG. 8.6. *Properties of materials at elevated temperatures showing how the tensile strengths vary as a function of temperature.*

Light-weight metals include Magnesium-Elektron alloys which contain magnesium and zirconium, and in more advanced classified alloys, magnesium, zirconium, zinc, and thorium. They have creep resistance up to 350° C and a specific gravity of the order of 1·8, together with high strengths at reasonably elevated temperatures. Ultimate stresses range from 15 to nearly 20 tons per sq in (2,300 to 3,000 kg/sq cm).

In the range of 150 to 370° C all the aluminium alloys and many magnesium alloys exhibit a very rapid and marked drop in tensile and compressive strengths and have very poor creep resistance. Stainless steels can be used but at a tremendous weight penalty. The most important recent discovery has been the development of thorium alloys of magnesium. These alloys retain good creep resistance and strength up to 370° C. Thorium magnesium alloys were developed by Magnesium-Elektron Limited of Manchester, England, as castings, but later Brooks and Perkins Incorporated produced sheet and plate varieties for airframe and skin uses. The magnesium thorium alloy can be deep drawn in a single operation and is readily spot and fusion welded. Anodic HAE coating can be applied and it has also been chrome plated.[11]

Then there is the possibility of using titanium[12] which is the fourth most abundant structural metal in the Earth's crust being fifty times more common than copper or zinc. It has about 56 per cent of the density of steel, while its ultimate tensile strength of 25 to 55 tons per sq in (4,000 to 8,500 kg/sq cm) can be raised to 70 to 85 tons per sq in (11,000 to 13,000 kg/sq cm) by alloying. In many applications its corrosion resistance is superior to that of stainless steel.

At ordinary temperatures titanium is covered by a protective layer which keeps it inert. This film dissolves at high temperatures and the metal then loses its passivity.

Its strength decreases with temperature and although it maintains useful properties above the temperature at which other light metals could be used, its effective limit is probably little higher than 500° C. But the progressive deterioration by oxidation beyond that point may be overcome in the future by improved alloys.

Titanium has roughly half of the elastic modulus of steel but has one which is greater than those of aluminium or magnesium, and it is non-magnetic. As the speeds of missiles increase and heating by air friction becomes a more pressing consideration, titanium may be used in greater quantities for skin and structure. For use in missile structure etc, it is alloyed with aluminium and manganese which achieves strength for a small sacrifice in ductility.

Pure titanium, although it has a high melting point of 1,660° C, creeps perceptively at room temperature under a stress of only 50 per cent of its ultimate strength. Alloys show better creep properties and some experimental alloys are even more encouraging.

Titanium is remarkably resistant to corrosion, even to hot nitric acid and aqua regia. At room temperature it has excellent resistance to red fuming nitric acid, but there are cases on record of serious explosions caused by RFNA in contact with titanium and titanium alloys, the causes of which have not yet been conclusively determined. Corrosion resistance is good also to mixtures of nitric and sulphuric acid. By good it is meant that the attack is less than 0·005 in (0·012 cm) per year.

Titanium cannot easily be welded or brazed because of the embrittlement produced by the ready absorption of hydrogen, nitrogen and oxygen. All these processes have to be carried out in an inert atmosphere.

Another material which might well be considered for missile structures is glass fibre phenolic laminate because in sheets of equal weight glass fibre laminate compares favourably with metal alloy sheets on a stiffness basis. At the same time, however, the shear strength and the modulus of the glass fibre laminate is less than those of the metals. There are many advantages to be achieved by the use of glass fibre materials in the guided missile industry. They are more resistant to fuel, oil, hydraulic fluids, etc., and are much less expensive to mould and produce in tapered thicknesses than are the metals. The tapered surfaces can be prepared quite easily with semi-skilled labour while the moulds and tools required for working the plastic structures are less costly than those required for working metals.

Plastic structures can be made quite large in size; for example, some mouldings for aircraft have been 17 ft (5·2 m) long, 6 ft (1·8 m) high by 3 ft (0·9 m) in width without stringers, bulkheads, or rings.[13]

Fibreglass reinforced plastics have a higher strength/weight ratio than mild steel, aluminium or magnesium. The temperature limits for laminated materials are known to now exceed the published figures. The great advantages of these plastic laminates are the low capital and labour costs which are especially important when we are considering the production of expendable guided missile. Articles can be formed on moulds made of low cost materials such as wood, plaster of Paris, light alloy or mild steel. Only low pressures and temperatures are required to carry out the work of curing. Complete shapes can be manufactured by a simple operation and much of the labour costs incurred in making metal components and assembling them can be avoided. But raw materials are still high in price and this somewhat offsets the labour saving. Use of plastics also reduces the tooling required to make the various components.

It is also possible to use asbestos-filled laminates at temperatures of up to 135° C, the ultimate tensile strength being 9,500 lb per sq in (670 kg/sq cm). With glass-filled laminates using phenolic resins, at temperatures up to 65° C, the ultimate tensile strength is 35,000 lb per sq in (2,500 kg/sq cm). However, glass-filled laminates with Malamine resins give, at temperatures up to 175° C, an ultimate tensile strength of 24,000 lb per sq in (1,700 kg/sq cm).

With glass-filled laminates having silicone resins there is no loss in mechanical strength at temperatures up to 250° C and no deterioration of the good electrical properties which are needed for the radomes of missiles. Even higher intermittent temperatures are possible. The ultimate tensile strength of this material is 20,000 lb per sq in (1,400 kg/sq cm) and it is recommended for uses requiring maintenance of electrical and mechanical properties at high temperatures.[14]

Indeed, the silicones appear to offer a number of advantages for guided missile uses. Silicone glass-cloth laminates have been moulded into components which have excellent anti-tracking properties, high impact strength, and are suitable for service at 200° C. Silicone elastic material remains flexible over the range from −90° C to +250° C and consists of a stable network of silicon and oxygen atoms. It can resist temperatures above and below the useful limits of other rubber-like materials and, therefore, finds extensive use in making heat resistant seals, diaphragms and tubings. Some grades decompose at flame temperature but they do not sustain combustion. In the case of silicone rubber the two molecular mechanisms which account for the properties react to alteration in temperature in opposite ways so that the net effect is small. It can withstand intermittent exposure to 300° C without damage. Silicone rubber can also be used in high voltage cables to prevent failure and a much thinner insulator and hence a lighter one can be used. Silicones are resistant to tracking flash-over which makes them useful for coating printed circuits. Silicone lubricants are also available which cover the range from $-70°$ C to $+250°$ C and are particularly useful for guided missile instruments which may have to function over a wide range of temperature. The small variation in viscosity with temperature also makes these fluids of great use for damping purposes in guided missile instrumentation. Silicone glass-cloth laminate forms a heat stable and a humidity resistant backing material for printed circuits. In addition it gives a useful cover of high strength for radomes in missiles.

Silicone laminates of glass-cloth have the following outstanding properties: they have outstanding heat stability, low thermal conductivity, good dielectric properties over a wide range of frequency and temperature, good mechanical properties and low specific gravity. One example of 0·125 in (0·32 cm) laminate has a tensile strength of 15 to 20,000 lb per sq in (1,400 kg/sq cm) and can be used up to a temperature of 250° C.

The most serious problem of aerodynamic heating, of course, is in the re-entry of the final stage of the intercontinental ballistic missiles. It has been shown[15] that with a laminar flow type of boundary layer the heat transfer rate might rise to fifty times that encountered in modern boilers, while for a turbulent boundary layer it could even be 1,000 times, that is 36×10^6 B.T.U. per hr per sq ft ($9·75 \times 10^7$ kg cal/hr/sq m). It may be possible to relieve this danger by reverse thrust devices but these are expensive in propellants; alternatively it may be possible to decelerate the missile as it re-enters by employing a large drag/weight ratio braking device.[16] Alternatively a method of transpiration cooling of the surface or even a boiling of the surface layers of the missile might be used. Taking an example of the passage of large meteorites through the atmosphere, it may be possible to arrange for melting of the surface to take place while the interior remains cool because of poor conductivity of the outer layers of the missile skin. In wind tunnels it has been found possible to melt bodies by aerodynamic heating and experiments are now proceeding to determine the optimum shape for the protection of bodies moving at hypersonic velocities.

It was mentioned earlier that the propellants might be used as a heat sink, but of course this is not possible during the re-entry phase of the trajectory. If the surface only is allowed to become hot while the interior remains cold, tremendous thermal stresses can be set up in a structure. These stresses can be damaging to supersonic wings because the materials are not available to withstand the great tensile stresses in the high temperature surface layers. The aerodynamic properties of the wing surfaces might be distorted so that the wings become useless.

Low expansion alloys will have to form the outer surfaces of these missiles; possibly it may be advantageous to use refractory ceramics, particularly the oxides of aluminium, magnesium, silicon and zirconium, because these can resist the oxidation of the atmosphere and do not appreciably weaken until near to their melting points in the region of 2,700° C. Although some metals have high temperature properties it is found that above 1,100° C many alloys fail as structural materials. One of the reasons is that the corrosion preventing elements which are alloyed in the metals are often precipitated and combine with other elements at the high temperatures and thus modify the structural properties of the material. (*Fig.* 8.7.)

Titanium is not a suitable material beyond Mach 4 and stainless steel is useless at Mach 7. Although tungsten, molybdenum and tantalum are possibilities they are much too expensive for use in expendable devices. But whatever the materials chosen it is important that they should lend themselves to ease of fabrication without expensive tooling and special equipment so as to minimize the cost of the weapon system, especially of the expendable missiles. It has been found possible to replace expensive heat resistant materials by using lower grade materials and surface treating them by dipping or spraying, sometimes by using special paints.

Machine-controlled processes must be aimed for in order to reduce production costs and also to improve component reliability. Exclusive or difficult manufacturing processes should be avoided. Airframes must be designed for ease of shipping, storage, and pre-flight assembly and testing. Power plants must be reliable and must consume the minimum weight of propellants. Guidance systems must be easily checked, be reliable, and be able to resist enemy countermeasures. The cost of the propellants is not an important criterion in missile power plants because each missile only employs one load of propellants and these usually cost only about 100th of the missile airframe and guidance. Their cost is accordingly not of very great

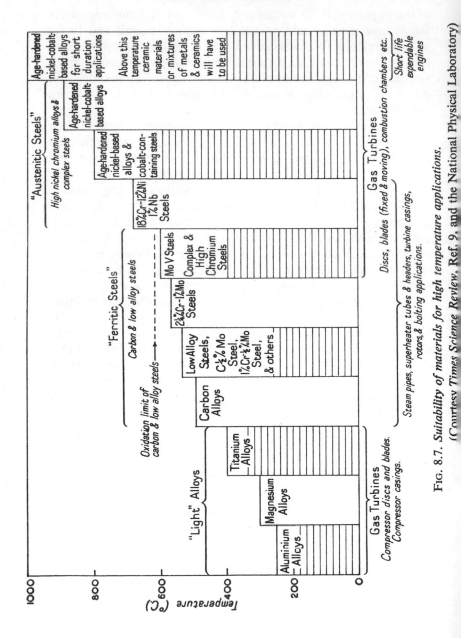

FIG. 8.7. *Suitability of materials for high temperature applications.*
(Courtesy *Times Science Review*, Ref. 9, and the National Physical Laboratory)

importance, but what has to be very carefully considered is the amount of space needed within the missile for the carrying of these propellants.

All missiles have nowadays some kind of terminal phase to the guidance procedure in which homing is used, and this calls for a search radar operating from beneath a radome through which the outgoing and incoming radar pulses must pass. The temperatures encountered in supersonic flight impose quite severe problems upon the radome structure as the organic resins which are currently used can seldom withstand temperatures encountered at high Mach numbers for any protracted period of time. In choosing materials which can operate under conditions of adiabatic heating in the boundary layer it has to be considered that the radome must give the minimum losses in energy by reflection, absorption, and scattering, and that as the pulses pass through the structure of the radome there must be

FIG. 8.8. *Mass production of rocket motors for a ballistic rocket vehicle.* (a) *A special tool developed for speeding the production of units with constant characteristics for the CORPORAL rocket.*

FIG. 8.8. (*b*) *A portion of a production line showing partly finished engines for this rocket missile.*

(Photos. Ryan Aeronautical Co.)

the minimum effects on the electromagnetic fields so that the major lobe of the radiation pattern from the aerial system is not distorted. A blunt nosed radome may have a transmission efficiency of between 90 and 97 per cent, whereas the pointed supersonic radomes may only have efficiencies of about 85 per cent.[17] For use in supersonic missiles it may be possible to employ glass and ceramics with special electrical properties or the fluorinated ethylenes such as Teflon.

In the coming years there is likely to be a levelling out of the guided weapon industry. After the current burst of activity by many firms pursuing diverse projects in an effort quickly to find solutions to the defence problem a gradual amalgamation of effort will take place. Even now concentration is being applied to a smaller number of weapons and this is likely to be reduced still further as sections of guided weapon technology reach individual high standards of efficiency and reliability.

FIG. 8.9. Research vehicles are also essential for the development of missiles. This photograph shows a small French research missile which is powered by a solid propellant rocket. It is the OPD320 and can carry 125 lb of instruments which are recovered by parachute.

(Photo. O.N.E.R.A.)

GUIDED WEAPONS

The final criterion in guided weapon development is that private firms should be supported financially by governments so that they can have sufficient finance available to attract the highly skilled technicians and scientists who are needed for the development of these weapon systems of a technological age.

TABLE 8.1 _Approximate Time of Production_

	Matador	V-2	Falcon	Fire-flash*
Project started	1946	1933	1947	1945
First test firing	1949	1934	1950	1946
Development completed	1951	1942	?	1955
Production started	1951	1942	?	1956
Deployment	1954	1944	1955	?

* It is assumed that the FIREFLASH started with the Fairey STOOGE missile.

TABLE 8.2 _Missile Production and Development_

Class of Missile	U.S.A.	U.S.S.R	U.K.	France	Switz.	Sweden
Surface-to-air	4*, 3	3*	2	2	1*	1
Air-to-air	3*	1*	2*	2	1*	1
Air-to-surface	1*, 3	?	1	1*	0	0
Surface-to-surface						
tactical	4*	1*	1	1	0	0
strategic	6	1*	1	1	0	0

* Indicates in production at 1 January 1956.

The figures for the U.S.S.R. assume that no new missiles have been developed in addition to German missiles which were taken over from Peenemünde and other sources.

REFERENCES

[1] HAVILAND, R. P., _Jet Propulsion_, **25**, 7, July 1955, 321–5.
[2] GREEN, C. F., Proc. Gassiott Committee, _Rocket Exploration of Upper Atmosphere_, Pergamon Press, London, 1954.
[3] KRAKAUER, M., BIBBARO, R. J., _Electronics_, **28**, 5, July 1955, 127–9.
[4] SHIVELENKO, D., _Jet Propulsion_, **25**, 9, Sept. 1955, II, 10S.
[5] STONE, I., _Aviation Week_, **59**, 14, 5, Oct. 1953.
[6] ANDERTON, D., _Aviation Week_, **52**, 21, 22, May 1950.

PRODUCTION AND DEVELOPMENT

[7] *Financial Times,* 27, Jan. 1956, p. 1.
[8] ADAMS, H. W., *ASME Paper,* 54A, 131, Dec. 1954.
[9] ALLEN, N. P., *Times Science Review,* No. 18, Winter 1955, 17–19.
[10] HUBBELL, W. G., *Aeron. Engineering Review,* 12, Sept. 1953, 31–36.
[11] ANON., *Magazine of Magnesium,* May 1955, 14–15.
[12] I.C.I. LTD., *Wrought Titanium,* Feb. 1955.
[13] BRAHAM, W. E., *Aeronautical Engin. Review,* 12, Sept. 1953, 37–40, 45.
[14] BAKELITE, LTD., *Technical Data,* Oct. 1953.
[15] MCLENNAN, C. H., *ASME Papers,* No. 54, A.57, Dec. 1954.
[16] NONWEILER, T. R. F., *Jnl. Brit. Int. Soc.,* 10, 1, Jan. 1951, 26–35.
[17] OLEESBY, S. S., *Electronics,* 27, 1, Jan. 1954, 130–5.

BIBLIOGRAPHY

Unguided Missiles

Mathematical Theory of Rocket Flight, J. B. Rosser, R. R. Newton and
   G. L. Gross, 276 pp. McGraw-Hill, New York, 1947.
Rockets, Guns and Targets, Ed. J. E. Burchard, Little, Brown & Co., 1949.

Guided Missiles

Ballistics of the Future, J. M. J. Kooy, J. W. H. Uytenbogaart, Technical
   Publishing Co. H. Stam, Holland, 1946.
Rockets, Missiles and Spacetravel, W. Ley, Chapman & Hall Ltd., London,
   1951.
Guided Missiles, A. R. Weyl, Temple Press Ltd., London, 1949.
Development of the Guided Missile, K. W. Gatland, Iliffe & Sons, London,
   1952.
V-2—The Shot into Space, W. Dornberger, Hurst & Blackett, London,
   1954.

Propulsion

Rocket Propulsion, E. Burgess, Chapman & Hall Ltd., London, 1952,
   1954. The Macmillan Co., New York.
Gas Turbines & Jet Propulsion, G. Geoffrey Smith, Iliffe & Sons, London,
   1955 (Sixth Ed.).

Instrumentation

The Gyroscope Applied, K. I. T. Richardson, Philosophical Library, New
   York, 1954.
Fundamentals of Transistors, L. M. Krugman, Chapman & Hall Ltd.,
   London, 1954.
Servomechanisms, J. C. West, English Universities Press Ltd., London,
   1954.
Frontier to Space, E. Burgess, Chapman & Hall Ltd., London, 1955. The
   Macmillan Co., New York, 1956.
The Elements of Navigation, C. H. Cotter, Pitman, London, 1953.
Principles of Guided Missile Design—Guidance, Ed. Grayson Merrill, D.
   van Nostrand Co., New York, 1956.

High Speed Flight

General Theory of High Speed Aerodynamics, Ed. W. R. Sears, Princeton
   University Press, 1954.

Materials

Strength and Resistance of Metals, J. M. Lessells, John Wiley & Sons,
   New York, 1954.
Fibreglass Reinforced Plastics, Ed. R. H. Sonneborn, Chapman & Hall
   Ltd., London.
An Introduction to the Chemistry of Silicones, E. G. Rochow, Chapman
   & Hall Ltd., London, 1947.
Wrought Titanium, I.C.I. Ltd., London, 1955.

INDEX

253